THE ANGRY OCEAN

Other books by Ronald Johnston

DISASTER AT DUNGENESS
RED SKY IN THE MORNING
THE STOWAWAY
THE WRECKING OF OFFSHORE FIVE

RONALD JOHNSTON

The Angry Ocean

HARCOURT, BRACE & WORLD, INC.

NEW YORK

B. 3.69

Library of Congress Catalog Card Number: 69-12039

Printed in the United States of America

CHAPTER ONE

It was immense. It was so big it was almost obscene. Now, its size was hidden by the patterns of the night, muted in the shadows cast by the shipyard lights and the reflections from the water. The ship seemed just a part of the scene, its identity lost in the whole composition of cranes and sheds, docks and gantries, unplated ribs and giant prefabrications. Only daylight would reveal it in all its vastness. The biggest ship the world had ever seen. Built to swallow half a million tons of crude oil in one great gulp, rush it across the seas, and spew it out into the thirsty cracking plants and tank farms of distant refineries.

Economically viable. That was the jargon the planners used to justify the building of this ship. And the money involved was so great, the rethinking of long held and proven business beliefs so basic, that they would have to prove themselves right. The jargon and the planning meant little to John Lang. To him, this ship was a challenge. Probably his last challenge before retirement, for he was within months of being sixty. But it was a challenge he feared more than any he had faced before. It was a challenge he need never have faced. He had wished it on himself.

That was his puritan way. Don't run from the things that frighten you. Face up to them. Overcome them. It was the way he had been brought up. It was the way he had run his life. The strict code, the rule of discipline, mind over matter. Here, in Japan, memories had stirred and nagged but, till recently, they had been checked by the menace of that monster lying quietly in the shipyard. That was how Lang thought of the ship. A monster. Huge, ugly, terrifying.

5

He leaned on the stone balustrade and looked down from his vantage point on the hill. He came here most evenings. It was like being on a ship's bridge. The rest of the world was there in sight and sound, but separate. More than forty years of separateness had made being alone important to him. Here on the hill, he had it. Shinoto was spread out below him. The shipyard, the steel mill, the neat rows of houses, the blocks of flats. The hospital, the schools, the shops. The hotel, the public baths, the brothels. Shinoto; one of the miracles of post-war Japan. It had been a small town, little more than a village, drawing most of its living from the fishermen who used the harbour. The American occupation forces took it over. It was in a fine position, the bay protected by headlands; there was plenty of deep water. Soon it became a major port with new breakwaters and jetties, the berths dredged out to take ocean going ships. Roads were laid, barracks built, an airstrip cut. Mr. Yashawa was said to have been in the scrap business before. An American base seemed like a good place to start anew. Even then he was called Old Yashawa. No one knew his age. No one knew anything about him.

Japan's steelmakers were crying out for scrap. Old Yashawa got the chance of some landing craft. He was not allowed to use the harbour so he ran them up on the beach at high water and had them cut up and hauled away before the next spring tide. It was a profitable deal. There were surplus trucks. Some he repaired and used; the others he broke up and sold. Then he bought an old cargo ship. He beached that and made a fine profit. There were lots of surplus ships. And trucks, and tanks, and aircraft. Yashawa Metal Products was in business. But the piles of scrap grew fast. Other people were selling scrap to the steelmakers. That was no reason for despair. Build a steel works at Shinoto, right next the stock-piles. That needed money. Not too difficult. The occupation forces were insisting on the breaking up of the old *Zaibatsu* cartels. Maybe they

6

would look kindly on competition. That's a word they like. They think competition cures everything. Yashawa got the money and Shinoto got its steelworks. It was small at first but very modern, very efficient, full of the new electronic marvels that did men's work quicker, better, and cheaper. Nineteen-fifty and the war in Korea. Business was good.

Then the blow fell. The Americans pulled out of Shinoto. The harbour emptied, the barracks emptied, the clubs and bars and brothels emptied. There were ceremonies; parades, speeches, bands playing, flags fluttering. The old man was not there. He was buying options on everything that was being left behind.

He had steel. In the harbour he had a graving dock. The fishermen needed new boats. Why not build boats in the graving dock? Then to launch them, all that was needed was to flood the dock. He built six big fishing boats that way. Then someone said the oil companies were thinking of building super-tankers; huge ships of 25,000 or even 30,000 tons. His engineers said it was possible. His was one of the first of this new breed of ships. Yashawa Steel and Shipbuilding was in business. It had led the way since then to even bigger ships. Buyers came from all over the world. They came from countries famous for shipbuilding. They came to buy because they could not compete in building time or price. The yard boomed and Shinoto boomed with it. Yashawa was an innovator but the town grew in the old Japanese way. He built houses for his workers, then flats as land got scarce, and schools and a hospital, a technical college, shops, a sports arena. Shinoto was Mr. Yashawa's town; every last beam and screen and *tatami* mat.

Now the latest miracle lay down in the shipyard. Lang's monster. Twenty times bigger than that first supertanker of fifteen years before. Twenty times bigger than that one some sceptical engineers in the West had claimed was dangerously big.

7

Lang shivered involuntarily as he gazed down at the blurred outline of his new command. He did not need to see it clearly to remember every detail. He had lived with it since it existed only on the drawing board. He was proud of it; of its size, its power, its immense complexity. He was proud that he had won the right to command it. But he was frightened too. Frightened that he was not big enough, young enough, able enough to stand down there on its bridge and live up to the new grand-sounding title he had won with his new ship.

Commodore Lang. It had a fine ring to it. It went well with his gaunt good looks. It only stated what was a fact. He was the senior captain in the Inoco fleet and the senior captain had always been given the honorary title of commodore captain. But Lang was the first to be called Commodore. It did not mark him out as a special breed of shipmaster. He wondered if, in fact, it marked him as a captain who was not a captain; for he was called Commodore Lang to distinguish him from the new ship's other master, Captain Stock. Stock was Lang's staff captain, in his mid-thirties, one of the new men being pushed up into the senior posts by Bruce in London; the push-button, fully transistorised, business school graduate sailors who were happier with a stopwatch or a critical path analysis than a marlin spike or a chipping hammer.

Lang heaved himself up erect, cleared his throat, and spat. Stock had that effect on him. They were poles apart in age and attitudes. Lang always thought of himself as a tolerant man. He had strong views but he did not impose them on others unless he saw that as part of his professional duty. But about Michael Stock there was so much he loathed that he could never disguise it. He was honest enough to remind himself that he had made this situation; that his pride, his determination to see a tradition upheld, had brought him this ship and Stock. But Lang was sure he was right. He had to be or all

8

his life meant nothing. He had lived by the rule book, and seniority was one of the rules.

It had all started just over a year before when the news broke that Inoco had decided to leap ahead from the 90,000 ton tankers to the breath-taking half million tonners. No, that was wrong. It had really started three or four years ago when James Bruce, youngest master in the fleet, with less than a year in command, had gone ashore as Marine Operations Director. That was the first break with tradition. Not that Marine Supers had always been chosen from the oldest and most senior captains. But they had always been senior and very experienced men. John Lang had become commodore captain only a few months before Bruce's appointment. He had worked and waited for forty years to reach that zenith only to find that he was the senior witness to the destruction of many of his professional values. Bruce had wasted no time. He quickly made it plain that the rumours running round the fleet about him were true. He had no time for romantic traditions; ships were industrial units and the same standards of efficiency would be expected as in storage depots, refineries, or research centres. Inoco paid high salaries and expected in return more than hand-made rugs, model ships and short stories. This vicious swipe at captains who, on ocean voyages, had little routine work to fill their day was a calculated insult to set the tone of Bruce's new régime. He was in a strong position. The tanker market was depressed. It was easy to say you would not stand for this sort of treatment; it was more difficult to find a new command in another company. And there was always that generous pension to think about.

So Bruce put his captains to work. When he said that word, work, you were reminded of his Scots background. The "o" was sounded as "u" and the "r" was doubled. It had an ominous sound to it. He wanted reports. Not just routine reports; reports according to a pattern he determined. Reports on the

9

organisation on board each ship, assessments of each job and a costing of it, suggestions for improving efficiency and lowering costs, suggestions for new designs and new equipment, new layouts and new manning scales. The captains buckled to. They surprised themselves. Their creaking brains started turning; their reports proved that they were looking at themselves and their ships in a new way. They typed up their reports, posted them off, sighed with relief and decided that the new broom had made its gesture. But their reports proved that they had looked only within the traditional framework. They had given Bruce just what he wanted; they had given him proof that a new approach was needed.

The captains woke up to find their ships swarming with efficiency experts, organisation and methods men, time and motion study teams. Not just in port. On passage at sea. These men were landlubbers, shorewallahs, hardly into the Bay of Biscay before they were puking all over the place. But their findings, piling up in Inoco's London office, revealed the real sickness. It was chronic; it called for radical surgery. It would take a little time.

New methods were tried, changed, perfected, then replaced with newer methods. The pressure was kept on the ships and the men but there were none of the revolutionary changes that had been predicted. Everyone breathed a little easier and confided in each other that Bruce had run out of steam, or more likely, been cut down to size by the big men in London and New York. The 50,000 tonners were followed by 90,000 tonners. The new ships were bigger but they were very much the same, size apart. Bruce still talked a lot. Lang remembered being thrilled, against all his instincts, listening to him. Bruce did not just talk. He was a spellbinder.

"Don't come the pompous shipmaster with me, Captain Lang. It rolls off me like water off an oily deck. You talk of tradition. I'm the one who wants to get back to tradition, not you. Your so-called tradition is recent, pale, puny. I want to see shipmasters like the men who ran the East Indiamen and the Clippers. Not just sailors, though they were bloody fine sailors, but merchants, entrepreneurs, thinkers, leaders. Right now, you're just a bunch of bus conductors; and at your salaries, you're overpaid. Yes, yes, I know it's the system. I know too that the system's going to change. With the kind of ships that are coming, we're going to need a new kind of man. We're going to need men who know what goes on behind all the buttons, men who know how business works, men who command respect for what they know, not for their gold braid and silver hair."

Now Bruce's dream was coming true. For Commodore Lang, it was a nightmare.

When the news had broken that Inoco was jumping over all the intermediate sizes and going for tankers of half a million tons, everyone realised that Bruce had not run out of steam. He had been quietly stoking his boilers. This decision was not just to build a ship or a series of ships. It meant new terminals, new harbours, new routes, new everything. For Lang it spelled out an attempt to strip him of the one privilege he really valued; the Commodore Captain's right to command each new ship as it left the shipyard.

Lang had survived the new régime thus far. Other masters had not. Some had settled for the smaller ships in the Mediterranean, the Caribbean, the West African coast; there they could see their time out quietly while the young men took the supertankers. Others had taken the bait of early retirement at the same pension they would have got at 60. A few, led by John Lang, had been stubborn. They went back to school to learn about electronics and computers, automation and business techniques. It was hard work. They had been away from books and learning for twenty, even thirty years. Lang resented every course he had to attend. But his determination not to be pushed aside helped him to study and learn and hold his head up among Bruce's whizz-kids. He brought out the first 90,000 tonner, *Inoco Prince*, then the *Princess*. It was when he came home on leave from the *Princess* that he heard the news of the new mammoth ship. The size appalled him but, perversely, he prayed that it would be launched before he reached retiring age.

He asked.

"About a year from now," Bruce told him. "They're fast, the Japs. Your time won't be up by then, will it?"

"No, no. I've still got more than a year. That's good. When will I be going out to Japan?"

"I don't think that'll be necessary, Captain."

"But you said this ship was going to be revolutionary. You can't expect men to go out there and take her to sea right away. You can't mean it. At least the senior men should be standing-by right from the time the keel's down."

"I'm planning for the whole crew to do just that."

"I don't understand. What's the use of everyone being out except the master?"

"He'll be there."

Lang stared. "Are you trying to tell me that I'm not getting this ship?"

Bruce smiled. "You make it sound like a disaster, Captain. Believe me, you wouldn't want this one. This one really is new. No, she's for the youngsters."

"She's mine, Bruce." His voice trembled with anger. "I'm the Commodore Master of this fleet. I get every new ship if I say I want it. I want this one."

"Sorry, Captain. The decision's made. Michael Stock's getting it. Trust me. I know what I'm doing."

"I wouldn't trust you as far as I could blow you."

"That's fighting talk, Captain Lang."

"Yes, it is. And I mean to fight this. I'm going to get this ship. You may be a big man, Bruce, but there are bigger ones in New York. I'm going over your head."

Bruce spread his hands. "You're entitled to do that. The best of luck."

Lang was at the door when Bruce spoke again. "There's a note in your file, Lang. More than once you've asked off ships bound for Japan. What's changed your mind?"

"Isn't it all in that secret file? I was a prisoner there for three years during the war. You know the war, Bruce, '39–'45. When you were still in short trousers."

"Oh, yes. I remember. Sweets were rationed. But you didn't answer my question, Captain. What's changed your mind?"

"Pride," snapped Lang.

"That's a noble emotion."

John Lang had not spent most of his working life as a cog in the Inoco machine without learning a thing or two about where the power lay. He wrote to New York. Not just to the parent company. He wrote personally to Eugene North, the director responsible for all the European subsidiaries. The reply came by return; it was friendly but gave nothing away. "Leave this with me, John," it said with the disarming familiarity of the Americans. It was three weeks before the next letter arrived. Lang looked at the air-mail envelope for minutes before summoning up the courage to open it. He read it, he read it again, then in an unlikely display of emotion, he danced round his flat yelling like a mad thing. He had won. The *Emperor* was his.

He was shown in to see Bruce as soon as he arrived at Head Office. "Have you heard from New York?" he demanded.

"About what?"

"About this," he said, spreading the letter triumphantly on the desk.

"Do sit down, Captain Lang." Bruce picked up the letter and read it.

Lang sat down, perching himself on the front of the cushion, watching for a sign. There was nothing; just that cold, forbidding look that was this man's face at rest.

Bruce laid the letter down. "Yes, I've heard." He smiled suddenly and his whole appearance was transformed. "My congratulations, Captain."

It was not what Lang had expected. "Well, eh, thank you." Then apologetically, "I'm sorry I had to go over your head. I don't like doing that kind of thing."

"Don't give it another thought, Captain. You were justified. You got what you asked for. And just at the right moment. We're starting briefing next week. It'll be pretty thorough. Probably last about three weeks. Then you can all go home for a fortnight before going out to Japan. My secretary will give you all the details."

"Thank you very much, Mr. Bruce. Sorry, I suppose I should say 'Captain Bruce'."

"Mister does very well. I'm not impressed with ranks."

"Good-bye then. I suppose you'll be at those briefings."

"Some of them, certainly. By the way, about ranks, there's something I wanted to tell you. We've decided that you should now be known as Commodore rather than Captain."

Lang said nothing, just nodded, but his face showed his surprise and pleasure.

"Yes, we've decided it will be a better arrangement. This way you won't be confused with your Staff Captain."

"My what?"

"Your Staff Captain. We've appointed Stock. He's agreed to the idea. We felt that with a ship of this size and complexity it wouldn't be fair to expect you to oversee all the fine detail when you already had the overall responsibility for the whole ship. It should work very well. It will take quite a bit of the load off you."

You bastard, thought Lang. You absolute bastard. It was a

14

full minute before he trusted himself to speak. "I'll be no figure-head, Bruce. I've been given this ship. I mean to command it."

"We expect that. Figureheads went out with sail. Good after-noon, Commodore."

That had all been almost a year ago. The briefings were held in the company's Administrative College down in the country, fifty miles from London. They had given Lang the first qualms about his new rank and responsibilities. The place had been a stately home which, without the proper aristocratic or historical associations, had failed to compete successfully for the trippers' half-crowns. Inoco got the house and forty acres at a very keen price. It was known to everyone in the company as Castle Brainwash.

The new ship had been launched on them with all the gim-mickry and stage direction of an improved detergent being shown to a soap sales force. The hall was set out with a desk and a chair for everyone. At the far end was a platform shrouded in a blue velvet curtain. The sound equipment was stereo so when the stirring march tune blared forth then faded as Bruce's taped voice took over, it was as if he was confiding into each ear in the auditorium. He ran quickly and expertly through the development of tankers. He touched on the economics of oil transport by sea. He mentioned the threat of the natural gas finds in the North Sea and the company's problem of holding down costs when its major reserves were in the Middle East, now having to compete with the flood of oil from North Africa in which it had no stake. He told them that a whole new concept had been decided on. It was called Project Emperor and would involve Inoco in vast reorganisa-tion and immense capital spending. Their part of this adventure was the new ship which gave the project its name. There would be more ships later but they and their ship were to be the pioneers. "Gentlemen, the *Inoco Emperor*."

The drapes slid silently back. The illuminated model sailed

in a sea of darkness. It was a bit of a let-down. It looked big but there was no reference to judge it by. Lang was relieved. It did not seem very different from any other ship. An improvement, really, for the bridge was back midships where it belonged not perched down aft as it was on the 90,000 tonners. The timed tape started up again. "Half a million tons. The biggest ship in the world." A few seconds to let that sink in. Then a spotlight picked out a familiar shape. "Almost as long as the Empire State Building is high." Another spotlight. "Half as long again as the height of the Eiffel Tower." A pause. "Broad enough to park ten Rolls-Royces bumper to bumper from port to starboard." The model listed magically to reveal the ten limousines parked nose to tail across its deck. "It's a big ship, gentlemen; she's all yours if you're big enough for her." The spotlights snapped off and the model sank down towards the platform then stopped, lit only by her own deck floodlights as she would be in port. "Yes, she's big but she looks very much like any other ship, size apart. She's not like any other ship. Inside, she's like nothing you've ever seen before." A back-projection screen glowed to life behind the platform. The picture showed an officer on the bridge taking sights with a sextant. "Out," said the voice, and a thick black cross cancelled the familiar scene. An engineer officer in white boiler suit reading gauges from the engine room floor. "Out" and the black cross showed again. Then an officer laying off courses on a chart, a man on deck spinning tank valves, a pumpman winding in an ullage tape, someone calculating with tables and graphs. For each picture, "Out" followed by that black cross. The series of slides covered almost every aspect of daily life on board ship; what was to replace it all was not revealed. There was a great void that cried out to be filled.

The last picture completed the destruction of all the things that had been held to be impossible of improvement. The last picture showed the manning structure of a supertanker.

The top box was marked "Captain" and spreading out below him the traditional departments; the chief officer and the chief engineer, the navigating and engineer officers in their various ranks, the radio officer, the bo'sun and the donkeyman, the pumpman, the quartermasters, the sailors, the oilers, the firemen. Then the catering staff headed by the chief steward, then the cook, assistant stewards, galley boy. It seemed impossible but inevitable. "Out."

The lights went on in the hall, the curtains slid back another three feet on each side of the stage to reveal girls in traditional Japanese costume. The tinkling of samisens came through the speakers. The girls hobbled daintily down the steps and moved among the desks, putting into each man's hand a leather bound book that was to become their bible. On the cover, etched in gold leaf, were two words, PROJECT EMPEROR.

The girl who came to Lang bent over and smiled. He nodded, took the book, and shivered as he caught the scent of her perfume. He looked across at Stock. He had glanced at him now and again during the performance. Each time the staff captain had been relaxed in his chair, that know-all smirk on his face. He was short, well built in a roly-poly way, his square fleshy face and the sandy hair already thin on top disguising his age. Doesn't even look like a shipmaster, Lang told himself, never mind act like one. No appearance, no bearing, no authority. Stock was speaking to one of the girls. She was smiling, then squealed as his hand found and nipped her bottom. Lang turned his head away, his neck suddenly hot inside his collar. He found himself looking directly at Bruce, who had appeared on a rostrum beside the stage. The Scotsman was smiling at him, lips closed. When everyone had a copy of the book, he spoke.

"Good morning, gentlemen. Well, all that was quite good for a bit of a giggle. Now let's get down to some real work."

For three weeks they had listened, talked and learned. Then

17

THE ANGRY OCEAN

a short holiday and out to Japan to start learning all over
again. Every piece of equipment going into the *Emperor* was
duplicated in that shed down in the docks. It was all hooked
up to a computer that could simulate every situation, every
emergency, every failure. Their brief had been to be ready for
anything and everything by the time sailing day came. That
was soon now. The day after tomorrow.

Lang closed his eyes tight against the scene below. Now
it really was all happening. There was no going back. He
turned and started down the hill. Right in his line of vision
was the hotel, towering over the town. The hotel was Mr.
Yashawa's pride and joy. Its Japanese name meant "the
meeting place of East and West"; everyone called it "The
Hotel." The design was fanciful but practical. There was a
fourteen story block, eight sided, each face showing a ladder
of balconies. From four of the faces, at ninety degrees to each
other, ran arms of only two story height. Between the south-
west and south-east arms the ground was laid out as an entrance
plaza. The quadrant to one side was a patio set with trees and
shrubs and a fountain, the other held an outdoor pool. On the
opposite side from the plaza, the ground led to the first tee of
the golf course which was still being constructed. Golf was
booming in Japan; a course designed by an international expert
would help to keep the hotel full. The tower block was a plush,
Hilton-style hotel up to the ninth floor. The five above that
were offices for the group of companies still mushrooming from
the original, uncomplicated Yashawa Metal Products. The
four arms offered Japanese style accommodation, parchment
walls, sliding doors, *tatami* mats on the floors, miniature furni-
ture, and trench type toilets to tax the thigh muscles of Euro-
peans. The whole place was a blending of East and West.
The meeting place of the two cultures was symbolised by the
huge tower rising from the intersection of the four arms. But
above it all, on top of the fourteenth story, was Yashawa's

penthouse. It was a surprise. It broke completely with the
smooth soar of concrete and glass; it had the scooped tiled roof
and drooping eaves of traditional Japanese architecture. From
it, not one square inch of the town, the shipyard, the mills, the
factories was hidden. The old man was up there, overseeing it
all.

Lang watched the soft glow of lanterns in the penthouse as
he walked down. He wondered what the mysterious old man
up there was doing. Was he watching now? What did he look
like? Was he the wizened old oriental of the movies, with skull
cap and kimono, counting up his loot on an abacus, looking
wise and inscrutable? No one could tell him. Everyone talked
about old Mr. Yashawa but no one would admit to having met
him. Except the charming Miss Odinoku. She met Mr.
Yashawa every day. She was his link with the world outside
his penthouse. But she could not answer Lang's questions. Or
would not. She claimed to know nothing of the old man's life
before he appeared at Shinoto after the war. Maybe that was
true.

Maybe, the commodore thought, the whole mystery of Mr.
Yashawa's real identity only exists in my mind. Especially
now, at night. It all seems crazy every morning when I wake
up, even though such sleep as I've had has been haunted
by that ancient terror. No, that's a lie. The terror's bad but it's
my own hate that haunts me. I thought it had died. Maybe
it's just being back in Japan after twenty-three years of trying
to forget. Maybe it's just never having seen Yashawa, never
knowing for sure that Major Kuno did die that night of the
bombing. Maybe it's just that Miss Odinoku reminds me of
that other Japanese woman. Maybe it's just because I know
about her and Stock. Maybe it's just that I'm a confused old
man, too small for that monster of a ship, too alone to do anything but hate and suspect.

Lang stopped and shut his eyes. He balled his fists, squeezing the mangled fingers that never let him forget for long his last stay in Japan. Come on, man, shake yourself out of it. You're just being sorry for yourself. Soon you'll be away at sea, away from this land. Only a couple of days. To-morrow, Eugene North and his wife arrive. He's the man who gave you this ship. He's a friend. All right, so you'll have to do what that public relations man, Grosset, says. You'll have to pose and talk to that horde of press and TV men. It can't last very long. Maybe it will be as easy as Grosset said. "There's nothing to it, Commodore. Just act naturally. Be like Mike Stock. He's getting to quite like it."

Of course he's getting to like it. That's what Stock's best at, playing a part. He'll be down there now with Grosset or some of the press boys, down in the red light district, boozing or wenching, or both. Dear God, give us it hard on this first voyage. Give us it really hard, then we'll see what the great Captain Stock does when dropping his pants is not enough.

The sky suddenly burst into redness. Lang stopped and looked. They were tapping a furnace over at the steel works. The whole town was drenched in a pulsing blood-red light. Shapes and shadows changed, the tower of the hotel shone like a great red candle, the sea beyond the harbour was for seconds like a moving field of poppies. Before the light faded the commodore saw his ship lying in its dock, etched out lividly in all its vastness.

Two thousand miles out in the Pacific, the sky was also red. There the redness was not man-made. There it came from deep down in the earth. An island was growing out of the sea. It had been growing for months. It was not a new phenomenon. It happened every year somewhere in the world. Sometimes an island peeped up above the ocean, fumed and smoked and coughed lava and ash, then sank back below the surface. Sometimes, times like this, the island went on growing, added to by the ash or lava boiling up from far below, spilling over, cooling and becoming land. This was a very special new island. It was special because of its position. It was strategic. It could become a new link in the outer ring of American bases stretching from Australia in the south to Alaska in the north. It could not have grown at a better spot if the Pentagon planners had chosen it themselves.

An aircraft had spotted it first. A U.S. navy ship had quickly been there. It was claimed in a ridiculous ceremony when a helicopter dropped a weighted flagpole on to the hot, soft ash. The flag burned away with the next cascade from the crater. It was immediately replaced. A few flags were a small price to pay for completing the ring round China. A Russian survey ship had arrived on the scene within weeks. Its interest was scientific. It seemed happy to let the Americans sit and watch their new island till it cooled down and hardened and its crater was snuffed out. The Russians had plenty to do containing China on the other side.

Phoenix Island, as the Americans had christened it in an unusual lapse from originality, was in no hurry to settle down. That night it was in good voice, roaring and rumbling and spitting out a thrilling display of fireworks.

CHAPTER TWO

The commodore had been right about Michael Stock. At that moment he was in a brothel with Grosset and a group of journalists. It was their last night on the town. Tomorrow evening there was the big party at the hotel, followed the day after by the launching. As soon as the last photo was taken and the last quote written down, the press men would be away in their jets to the next story. Stock was a favourite of theirs. He was good company and he could always turn up with something worth saying. He knew the new ship inside out and had the knack of explaining it without all the technical jargon. He also had an inexhaustible fund of dirty stories.

They had started at the hotel after dinner. But the bars there did not promise the kind of evening they were after. Prostitution in Shinoto had two faces; the traditional one with thick white make-up and black painted teeth, hair scooped high in combs and clips, colourful kimonos and flat sandals; and the other face, the legacy of foreign occupation, with lip-stick and mascara, permed hair, tight sweaters, short skirts, and stiletto heels. Each face had its place; the traditional in the wood and parchment houses of the red light district, the modern in the downtown cabaret clubs.

The eight men were in one of the traditional houses. The party was not going well. The madam had miscalculated. She had thought to excite some business by putting on a strip show. There was something oddly obscene about a woman in the formal dress of old Japan peeling off her clothes. Everyone sensed it. The men, squatting on the floor in a circle, fidgeted and drained their drinks and fetched for cigarettes. The women, distributed one to each man, sat back on their heels and glanced about furtively. The party was saved by an uninvited guest.

He pranced into the room and struck a pose. He was Japanese, in his twenties. He was in vest and underpants. He was high on *sake* and was now topping himself up from a bottle of Japanese whisky which he waved above his head. "*Banzai*," he shouted, and charged round the room. Again "*Banzai*," this time doubling his fist and bending his forearm in phallic symbolism. Another warrior-like charge, another "*Banzai*," and all the time he was grinning from ear to ear. He started pouring whisky into the empty glasses. His deserted woman

22

appeared at the door, beckoning him out. He waved her away, went on pouring whisky, then stood holding the bottle aloft to make his toast. Everyone got the message. "*Banzai*," they all roared and downed their drinks. Someone called for more whisky. Chatter and laughter broke out. The madam sent for the liquor. She was relieved. It had been a bad moment. The whisky came. It was the same brew as the erstwhile *samurai's* but it was in branded Scotch bottles. Mike Stock was relieved too. He would not have left a dead party. Now, with the whole thing going again, he looked for a way to escape.

He never visited brothels except for visual entertainment, and then only as one of a group. He found them depressing places. They were sometimes good for a laugh but not for anything else. Not for him. There were people who would offer an explanation. "Why pay for it when you can get it free as easily as he can?" But it went much deeper than that. Stock found it convenient to maintain several faces on the world. The one that stuck was the dirty one. The one that stuck about his private life was the one Lang believed. Whoremonger and boozer. Neither was true.

Mike enjoyed a drink but he had never come to terms with the throbbing head and foul tongue that came the next day after heavy drinking. He knew about people though. He knew the silly conventions about taking drink for drink. He felt that people he liked deserved to have their illusions preserved. So he drank drink for drink. Or at least he appeared to. He was an expert at disguising his consumption. He was helped by not needing alcohol to make him jolly, funny, fluent. All that came naturally to him. But since he liked being with people it all added up to a reputation as a heavy drinker with the special advantage of never suffering a hangover.

In the renewed hubbub of the party he was thinking about Kim. She would be at the hotel now, waiting for him. He liked people a lot but he liked being with her more. He had to get

23

away. He chose the illusion-preserving way. He touched the woman next to him and got to his feet. She nodded and stood up. Someone noticed them at the door and shouted. A chorus of encouragement followed them into the corridor. He slipped some money into her hand and hurried away, his sandals flip-flopping on the bare wood. She was puzzled, called after him, but he kept going. Along the corridor, down the stairs, kicking off the sandals and selecting his own shoes from the collection at the door. The air outside was cool and clean-smelling after the heat and smoke and scent inside. He took a deep breath and smiled to himself. Kim would be waiting. He straightened his tie and ran a hand across his sparse hair as he started walking back to the hotel.

She was there in his room in one of the Japanese wings. It was his room but for months they had called it "our room." It was typical of Stock to choose to live there rather than in the suite that had been reserved for him in the tower block. He liked exotic surroundings. He particularly liked Japanese rooms. They gave a feeling of space and light and lack of clutter.

Kim looked up as he slid back the door. She was kneeling on a big quilt in the middle of the floor. She put down her book and smiled. "Where have you been, Mike-san? I've been waiting."

"Sorry, my love. Had to do my duty and keep Grosset and his pals happy." He went over and bent down and kissed her.

"You've been drinking."

"Not much. You know me. I'd like a drink now. I'd like tea. Would you make some?"

"Of course."

He picked up the kimono she had laid out ready for him and crossed the room. He slipped off his jacket and stripped off his shirt. He shivered as the cold silk of the sleeping robe

24

touched his back. He watched Kim out of the corner of his eye. The charcoal in the *hibachi* was glowing under the kettle. She was arranging the utensils for the tea making. The two bowls, the vase of dry tea, the ladle, the whisk. She did it all with grace and economy of movement. This formality was something they both enjoyed. Whether it was tea making, or cooking *suki-yaki*, or meeting each other, or saying good-bye, this formality was there. It seemed right and proper, it was not cold or stilted, it was a sign of closeness and familiarity. She was waiting now, doing nothing till he was changed and sitting opposite her. She looked demure, head bowed, her hair held up at the back with a comb, her hands folded in the lap of her kimono. Now she looked wholly oriental. But outside this room it was difficult to be sure she was Japanese. She wore western clothes and she wore them with great flair. Her black hair was shoulder length, turned in at the neck. Her make-up disguised her eyes which glowed brightly when the heavy lids were drawn back. Outside, she looked what she was; a modern, sophisticated career woman, a product of Tokyo's Women's University, a brilliant economist holding down a responsible job in the Yashawa headquarters. Mike Stock liked her in both roles. Alone, together, in their room, he liked her this way, acting the part of the submissive, your-wish-is-my-command oriental woman.

He pulled his gown round him and tied it off. He looked down and smiled when he saw his feet. They were in the flat sandals required of everyone in the Japanese wings but they were still covered with brightly striped socks. Kim had laughed when she first saw him stripped but for socks and sandals. How long ago was that? A few months, almost a year, a life-time. The socks were now one of their secrets, one of the little rituals of their love. He went over and sat down cross-legged in front of her.

She made tea. Each movement was exquisite; holding the

bowl, measuring in the tea, ladling the hot water, spinning the bamboo whisk, offering the steaming bowl. Their fingers touched for a second as he took it from her. He held it, feeling the warmth through the fine china, smelling the fragrance, waiting for her to make her own. They sipped without speaking till the bowls were empty.

"That was wonderful, Kim. Thanks. I feel like a new man."

"That's good."

"What's the matter, my love? You look a bit down in the mouth. You all right?"

She nodded. "I suppose so. I was just thinking. It won't be long now."

"As the man said to his friend in the cold shower." He grinned.

She smiled sadly. "It's not really funny, Mike. You know what I mean."

He bent forward and took one of her hands in his. "I know, Kim. But it had to come. We've known all along. I'm a sailor. Ships have to go to sea. Ships need sailors." He waited but her eyes stayed down. "It's not really so bad, you know. It'll only be a few months before we're back for the guarantee. It'll just be like when I went home on leave a couple of months ago. We survived that."

She nodded her head. Yes, we survived that, my Mike-san. You came back and we started again where we'd left off and you told me about your wife and your children and what you had done with them on your holiday. I lay in your arms and listened to you and was happy because you were happy, because you were back, and thrilled all over when you touched me, and felt frightened because I was an incident, because I only owned a part of you that was not permanent.

"Come on now, Kim. Cheer up. Tell me what you've been doing today. Been busy?"

26

She looked up and smiled, her lips parting this time to show strong white teeth. "Busy of course. I don't know how I got mixed up with this launching ceremony. I'm supposed to be a back room girl. Now I seem to be a one-woman public relations team."

"Old Yashawa's shrewd. That's why he's been such a success. He can always pick the right man, sorry, woman, for the right job."

"Maybe. I'll be glad when it's over and I can get back to my proper job. I don't like public relations. I don't like your Mr. Grosset."

"Who does? He hasn't been bothering you, has he?" There was a sharp edge to his voice.

"Now Mike, there's no need to go and punch him on the nose or whatever it is you do. No, I just don't like him. He fawns over me, he's always looking at me in that way. You know, I suppose he knows about us. He makes me feel cheap, dirty. I know it's silly of me."

"Forget about it, Kim, love. He's just a long haired pretty boy who fancies himself. He's only jealous of your efficiency. And pleased too because if everything goes right tomorrow and the next day, he'll get the credit. He's that type, he's a climber. He hasn't got what it takes so he climbs up on other people's backs."

"I know all that, Mike. I'm just easily upset. It's the same with the commodore. No, not the same; he's such a gentleman. But he keeps asking me about Mr. Yashawa, what he looks like, everything. And now these midnight phone calls. It all upsets me. I suppose I'm on edge all the time now just because I don't want you and me to finish, Mike."

"Come here, you silly, gorgeous Japanese girl." He reached out and pulled her across the quilt and put her head against his shoulder. "Now you listen to me. Forget about Grosset and old Lang. Forget about everyone. Except us. For we're not going to finish. We've got tonight, and tomorrow night, and maybe the night after. Then there's a wee break and I'll be back with the ship for the guarantee. Then there'll be the next ship and I'll be back to train the crew here. Believe me, my love, we're not going to finish. We're special." He looked down at her. Her robe was gaping where it crossed below her neck. There in that deep shadow were those firm high breasts. His mouth dried.

She pressed her face into his chest. That's right, Mike-san. Keep on telling me that. That's what I want to believe. I know we won't, can't, but I can go on believing it. Was this what they meant by women's rights? Women's rights, emancipation, romantic love, freedom of choice; all these foreign ideas imported with the occupation, taught, lauded, recommended through school and university. Fools. What rights are left to a woman in love? A woman in love with a man committed for life to someone else? Two rights. To give, to love, to be loved, to savour the moment and ignore the future. Or to resist, to go away, to stifle it all. Either way, torture. Kim's way was the first way. To let it happen, to enjoy every precious moment, knowing that some day it would all end. But that way, there was no final answer. That way, you began to believe it would never end. Like now, with time running out and Mike already talking of coming back in a few months. Kim wanted permanence but she knew that marriage with Mike was impossible. If it had been possible, she would have shied away. She was adult and intelligent. She had seen romantic marriages; she had seen the magic die. In the ones that lasted she had seen the magic transmuted into bare tolerance. Maybe that was how it had to be. She wanted none of it. She wanted none of Mike's kind of marriage either. It seemed happy enough. In his way, he seemed very fond of his wife. He adored his two little girls. That was funny, him having only girls. He was such a masculine man. Or was he? Could he be wholly masculine

28

and still have his instinctive understanding of women? Wholly masculine or not, he certainly needed women. At home in England it was his wife, here in Japan it was Kim, somewhere else it would be someone else. Does his wife know? Kim wondered. Does she care? Or is she like me, grateful for what she's got? She should be. She's got more than me; she's got him for ever. But if I had him for ever, I'd never share him.

She cuddled in closer and felt his arm round her. But I've got him now, at this moment. This is worth having, being able to sit close to someone, feeling at peace but knowing that any time passion may erupt. Knowing that there is no hurry, knowing that when the time comes it will be all right. Mike will see to that. He is that kind of lover.

Kim had been a wartime baby. She qualified by a few days; she was born a week after Pearl Harbor. She remembered nothing of it. Her family lived out in the country away from the cities and the bombing. Her father was a minor civil servant. They were not well off but they were not poor. Towards the end of the war there were shortages but they did not touch the little girl. Her parents saw that she had enough to eat. When the war ended and the occupation began and the rebuilding got under way, her father was moved to Tokyo. It was promotion; they were better off. But the little girl did not think that; she thought the crowded bomb-scarred city was horrible after the country. She was the age for school. That was horrible too at first. There were crowds of children and noise and new rules. The new rules were the biggest problem. She had spent her first five years under the strict family rules of old Japan. These rules still persisted at home. But the schooling of old Japan was finished. The occupation brought with it foreign ideas, American ideas, and the children were the target. Give me the child at school and I will give you the completed man. Or woman. There would be no more wars when everyone knew that democracy was the greatest.

The little Kimauko Odinoku soon proved as adaptable as any other child. She followed the school rules at school and the old rules at home. But seeds were laid. As she grew through girlhood to adolescence she found herself being sorry for her mother. The new liberties did not touch Mrs. Odinoku. She knew her place. She ran the house and looked after her husband and children. She preferred it that way. In her teens Kim was ready to experiment. She argued at home, she argued at school, she marched in student demonstrations. She had got the message. It was not quite the message that had been intended but children seldom read messages the same way as their elders. Children themselves get the messages mixed up. The idea of romantic love was blossoming among Japan's youth like wild flowers on a bomb site. Kim liked the idea. It gave her a status like Western women. But romantic love and free choice meant free love to a lot of boys. It only took a few inexpert fumblings in dark corners to guide Kim to what she hoped was the real thing.

It did not come quickly. She was in no hurry. She was now at university and doing well. When it did come it had all the hallmarks of a fairy tale. He was a lecturer, young, handsome, a clean cut American boy. They dated. He was very proper. The second time, they kissed. Soon they wanted more than kisses. That was the end of the illusion. It was no one's fault. He was a taker. He could not give. It was as if she had been dropped into an ice cold bath. But the shock was soon replaced with a maternal feeling. He was like a baby in her arms. It was a short-lived affair. Kim was not happy playing mother in bed.

That had been that for a long time. She graduated with a high mark and came to work for Mr. Yashawa. She liked him. He was a Japanese who understood and tolerated, even enthused, about foreign ideas but he remained wholly Japanese. He liked Kim. He gave her her head at work and she, free of entanglements, quickly became an important cog in the old man's empire.

Till now. Till the end of last year when the new ship was started and the crew came out from Britain. She had met Mike that first day. She remembered noticing his eyes. They were special; big, deep, penetrating, full of humour. That was the only thing that was special about him. He had been in civvies, his suit rumpled, his tie askew, his thinning hair straggling in the wind. He was short, plump, a humpty-dumpty of a man. Certainly not the great lover. The rest was now history. She had been right all along. There had been a man she could love, who could love her, make her feel like a goddess. Of course he was married. He had never hidden that from her. Over and over again she told herself that did not matter. It was just as well. This kind of feeling could not last for ever. But she wished it could.

They were lying together on the quilt. She could feel his hand, gentle on her breasts. She opened her eyes. He was there, close, his eyes shut, his face relaxed as if in sleep. The light from the lantern showed the stubble on his chin. Was that special too, that they did not put out the light? They did not need darkness. Don't go to sleep, my Mike-san. I could too, easily. But not now, not tonight, with so little time left to us.

She put out a hand under his robe. He stirred. I might have known. He's playing tricks on me again. It's going to be all right. As always.

CHAPTER THREE

Stock swore as the telephone started ringing. Kim tried to turn away out of his arms. He held on to her. "Let it ring. It's probably a wrong number. Let it ring."

Kim struggled and sat up. "It's no use, Mike. You might as well answer it. You know what happened the last time. First the porter knocking at the door, then the commodore himself."

"Yes, yes, and you were all embarrassed."

"Yes, I was. I can't help it, Mike. I've told you before. I love you. I want to share this room with you. I don't care who knows it. Everyone does by now. But it's different when someone's outside the door and knows I'm in here with you. I know it sounds silly."

Stock was hunting for his slippers. "It certainly does. But that's woman's logic, I suppose." The phone was still ringing. He grabbed it up, bawled "All right," and slammed it back on its rest. "I don't know what's got into the old bastard. This is the fourth time this week. He must have taken a fancy to you, Kim, the way he's trying to make sure we get nowhere fast. You been leading him on or something?"

"That's not funny."

He found his slippers and stabbed his feet into them. "Nothing's funny, love. For months all he did was scowl at me when you were around; now all of a sudden he starts ringing me up in the middle of the night. He's a nut, I tell you. He wants to save all the women of the world from a fate worse than death. He doesn't see me when he looks at me. He sees the devil complete with horns, and a tail with an arrow on the end pointing to the bedroom."

"Well?"

Stock shook his head and laughed. "I asked for that, didn't I."

Kim nodded. "Thank goodness, Mike. I thought we were going to fight."

He walked over and put his hand under her chin. "Not us, Kim. Maybe a little lovers' tiff now and again. But never fight." He bent down and kissed her. "Don't go away. I won't be long."

Stock's good humour only lasted into the corridor. As he shuffled along towards the lifts up the tower block, his round face was set in a hard mask. He felt he had gone as far as he could in his brief from Jim Bruce to jolly the commodore along. He had done that, and it had not always been easy, on the ship, in the yard, in the training shed. This new interference with his personal life was outside all that. It was not himself he worried about. People had been trying to reform him all his life. He could take that. But this was hurting Kim. That was outside his book of rules.

Going up in the lift, he wondered what the excuse would be this time. It was always some query about the ship or the equipment or the crew. It was always carefully chosen to seem genuine. It was always preceded by an apology for the lateness of the hour. It was all terribly civilised. He got out at the ninth floor and walked along to Lang's room. He knew he should play it cool. All sweetness and reason; "don't worry, Commodore, your wish is my command"—"no, I wasn't sleeping" —"no, I wasn't busy with anything else." That was how he had played it before. He had had to choke back his anger and, as a result, was less than jolly company afterwards. This time there would be no sweetness and reason. This time there was going to be one whale of a row.

He flung open the door and walked in. "Well, what the hell is it this time?"

33

Lang was sitting at his desk. He turned and stared. "Don't you ever knock before coming into a room, Captain?"

"You've got some nerve, Lang, talking about manners."

"Close the door, Captain Stock. Please."

Mike slammed the door with his foot and the whole room shook. "Is that closed enough for you?"

The commodore swung round in his chair and faced Stock. "Captain, if I had had the chance on the phone, or just now, I'd have apologised for calling you out so late. Since you gave me no chance, I find your boorish conduct inexcusable."

"Are you finished?"

"No, I'm not finished. I'd appreciate in future if you dressed properly instead of wandering round the hotel looking like something that's escaped from Gilbert and Sullivan."

Mike hitched his kimono tighter round him and retied the knot. "Very funny. Now it's my turn. There won't be any future midnight matinees. I've jollied you along for months, Lang. Particularly, I've jollied you along since you started needing company in the middle of the night. That's what Bruce told me to do. 'Jolly the old chap along.' Well, I've done it. As much as I'm going to. I'm warning you now. You try it just once more and you'll be looking for a new staff captain."

"That would be a pleasure." Lang was very angry.

"No, Commodore, it wouldn't be a pleasure. You're stuck with me, and on my terms. For once in my life, for a few months yet, I'm indispensable. Without me, that ship down there's a non-starter. But she wouldn't miss you."

"I don't like being threatened, Stock."

"And I don't like being pestered. Just get down off my back, Commodore, and you can relax and enjoy your last trip." He walked across the room and pulled back the curtains.

Lang sat erect in his chair, his mangled fingers digging into the chair arms like a bird's claws grasping a perilous perch.

Mike stood at the window. He could pick out the window

of his own room far below in the Japanese wing. He had said his piece. He had shut Lang up. When he spoke again, his voice was quiet, almost as if he was talking to himself. "Why d'you do it, Lang? What d'you get out of getting me so mad that I lash out at you? You know I must win. That's the way it's been set up. I'm the key man. Maybe that's what you resent. You've got the fifth stripe but I've got the last word. No, it can't just be that. It's not too bad during the day. It's only at night. And only recently. What is it, Commodore? Do you stand here at this window and watch that other window down there? Do you wait for the light to go out then reach for the telephone? That's no good, you know. Half the time, we don't bother to put out the light. I suppose you think that's indecent. No, I think you think I'm indecent because I'm married and Kim's not my wife. You're wrong, you know. What Kim and I've got is pure compared with a lot of marriages. You wouldn't understand that, of course. Or would you? Maybe it's her that bothers you. Maybe you knew someone like her once. Is that it? Japanese? Seems unlikely. Last time you were here, you were a prisoner. Or maybe you just hate all Japs. That would figure. They certainly made a mess of your hands. But you lived. Lots didn't. So what's it all about, Commodore?"

Lang said nothing, just sat very still in his chair.

Stock pulled the curtains shut and walked over and pulled up a chair. It was as if Lang was in a trance. "What's it all about, Commodore? D'you want to talk?" He tapped the older man's shoulder.

Lang came to with a start. He stared at Mike, blinking his eyes.

"I was asking you what it's all about, Commodore."

"Oh, oh yes. Sorry to get you out so late, Stock. I wanted to ask you about something. What was it? Oh yes, that midship joint."

"What about it?"

35

"I don't seem to have any dock test reports on it."

"That's right."

"Why not?"

Mike took a deep breath. The new expansion joint was one of Lang's recurrent nightmares. It was the first of its type. Before the *Emperor*, ships had been built with a keel that bent and stretched with the stresses of sea and cargo. It had worked well enough but, as the length of tankers grew, the problem of structural failure grew ominously. Several solutions were under test. The Yashawa system, the *Emperor*'s system, joined the fore and aft sections of the ship so that they overlapped. The area of the overlap worked like a piston moving in a cylinder. When the ship was hogged or sagged in a seaway, one section slid in and out of the other, the movement being damped and controlled hydraulically. It was revolutionary.

"Why not?" repeated Lang.

"I thought I'd explained that already, Commodore. All we've been able to do is test it for movement, tightness, pressure, that sort of thing. On trials we'll be able to hog and sag her with the ballast. If we're lucky we'll get a bit of a swell and get some readings that way too."

"Seems damned hit or miss to me. After all, that thing's holding my ship together."

"Quite right, Commodore. But what d'you want me to do? The thing's been tank tested to destruction a dozen times. All the results say it'll stand up to a wave a hundred and fifty feet in height. The highest recorded wave in history is ninety-three feet. What more do you want?"

"Models. What good are models?"

"It's all there is. Can I go now?"

"Yes, yes, of course. Thank you for coming up. In the morning, have a word with the yard. See if they can suggest any more tests for that joint."

"Anything you say, Commodore." He opened the door. "If

36

I might make a suggestion, just forget about that joint, forget about me, forget about Miss Odinoku, forget about everything and get some sleep. Good night."

Lang sat staring at the door. Forget about that midship joint. Yes, I can do that. Forget about Stock. Yes, I think I could almost do that. Forget about Miss Odinoku. No. No, I can't forget about her, or about who she reminds me of. And I can't forget about Mr. Yashawa and who he might be. I know it's all crazy and impossible but, now it's in my head, I can't get rid of it. It's not so bad during the day. It gets worse as the evening grows into night. Then everything's quiet and it all seems possible. Sometimes it seems absolutely certain. And it's much worse now that time's getting short. Only another day, a day and a half in this country. It should worry me less, knowing that soon I'll be away, never to return. But it's worse. Before I go, I must know for sure. I must settle it once and for all. He pressed his fingers into his eyes and felt the mangled ends on his lids. He pulled them away and stared at them. No wonder I can't forget. No wonder I can't stop hating.

Lang's war was lucky until late on in 1941. He had been in tankers all the time but he was never torpedoed or mined or bombed. He was chief officer then. He had watched dozens of ships die. Slowly, as the water poured in; instantaneously, as explosives detonated; flammably, as petrol spread and caught light and burned. But it never happened to one of the ships Lang was on. Not till that day deep in the South Atlantic when the raider came. Even then the death of the ship had a sort of formal decency impossible in the sudden attack by submarine or aircraft. There was no chance of escape. The code books were put in their weighted bag and dumped before the boarding party arrived. The cargo was no use as fuel for the raider so the crew were taken off and scuttling charges laid.

The German captain was apologetic about having to sink the ship. It was the way of war. The officers and men would, of course, be treated with proper courtesy. Conditions might be a little primitive but that was unavoidable. Civilised, that was how Lang thought of that captain.

All things considered, the prisoners' treatment on the raider was exemplary. Far south they steamed, round the southern tip of Africa into the Indian Ocean. Then they were transferred to a tanker which fuelled and stored the raider. Conditions on the tanker were more primitive. The crews of three ships, over ninety men, were imprisoned in the hold up near the bow. Exercise on deck was restricted and always under guard. It was very hot down in that hold in the tropics. But there was food and water for all and medical attention for those who needed it. Mad schemes were hatched for escape but they were never more than mental exercise for the prisoners. Lang took no part in these games. He did not like being a prisoner any more than the others. But his captors were doing their best to treat him properly. They were civilised men caught up in a war.

December 1941 and Pearl Harbor. The guards told them of each new Japanese victory. The tanker now had not just a friendly country to run to in an emergency; it had an allied country. It ran at full speed for Japan; it needed fuel and stores and it wanted to be rid of its prisoners. They came ashore in Japan early in 1942. Conditions in the camp were not all they might have been but they were far better than in Japanese prison camps away from the home islands. There was not a lot of food but there was enough rice to stay alive on. The men thinned down but did not starve. The guards were reservists, called back to free younger men for the fighting. Discipline was strict but not harsh for those who obeyed the rules. There were a few wild spirits who did not and were penned for days at a time in a bamboo cage out on the parade ground. Lang had no sympathy for them. Rules were rules to him.

Everyone had to work. It got them out from behind the wire. Some worked in factories, some on the land, some down on the docks. That was where Lang worked, loading and unloading ships and barges. It was hard work but it kept him reasonably fit. Self preservation became more and more important to him. He was going to see the war through and survive. He had no love for his captors but he did not hate them in the way many of the men did. It was the way of war. He was going to survive.

He had to survive a long time. 1942. 1943. 1944. Into 1945. The tide of war turned against Japan. Rations shortened in the camp. There was a lot of sickness. Everyone lost more weight. Lang was very thin; he could count his ribs, his hip bones were so thinly covered it was a relief to get up in the mornings from his straw mattress. But he could still work. A lifetime of strict discipline had given him a strong body. He was still going to survive. He was not popular in the camp. He was a solitary man, always had been. There were those who thought he was too willing to work. A few wondered if he passed on information to the Japanese. He preferred to be left alone. The other prisoners made sure he was.

In the spring of that last year of the war, something happened that helped Lang in his determination to see it through. It was a small thing but it became big in his mind. He was working in the docks. Security had been tightened. The war was coming nearer home. There had been raids on the docks. There were wrecks in the harbour, burned out hulks tied up to buoys. There was talk that there had been sabotage too. It was then that Lang first noticed the woman. She was Japanese, she worked there too. He never knew her name. Her age he could only guess. She might have been as young as her twenties or as old as forty. It did not matter. She became a sort of symbol to him.

That first day, he was squatting during a break period. The

39

men were weak. Breaks had to be frequent. He was apart from the others. The guards did not bother much about him. He was reliable. He looked up and saw her gazing at him. She was ten, fifteen yards away on the edge of a group of women workers. She dropped her eyes as soon as he noticed her. He went on staring. There was nothing in her appearance to set her apart from the other women. She wore the same drab working clothes. But Lang thought he had seen something special in her eyes. She looked quickly at him again then turned away. There was no more time. The guards were blowing their whistles to start work again. That quick glimpse of her face stayed with him all through the afternoon. And through the evening back at the camp as he lay on his mattress. He had no idea why the image stayed in his mind. Did it remind him of his mother? That seemed impossible. It was an oriental image. Did it remind him of a picture or a face marked briefly in a crowd? He did not think so. He knew it was not a face or a look that reminded him of any woman he had known intimately. He had known none. In all his thirty-six years he had kept himself apart from women. He could see their beauty, understand how men could enjoy being in their company; but the idea of going to bed with them repelled him. That was for men like his father; for lechers and whoremongers. The only woman he knew at all well was his mother. Women were to be admired, respected, pitied, and supported in the troubles men brought to them. He wondered about his mother that night. He wondered if she knew he was still alive and a prisoner. He wondered if she was maybe dead. It was a long time now. She was not an old woman but her life had aged her before he could afford to start providing for her. And there was the war, the blitz and all that. He had had no letters. But few ever got through.

The next morning Lang was keen to get down to the docks to work. He liked the mornings; the sight of a fresh new day heartened him. Springtime helped. It was the time of the cherry blossom; even a brief long view of the mass of pink and mauve petals brought a lift to the drab routine of prison camp and work. That morning it was the woman he wanted to see. She came later than the prisoners. Her gang was working on a barge farther along the quay. At the midday break he separated himself as usual and squatted as near as he dared to that barge. She saw him but pretended not to. It was as if she understood. When she did glance at him, she held his eyes for a second or two, then gave him a tiny smile as she turned away.

It went on like that for weeks, almost three months. Sometimes she would leave a piece of dried fish or another titbit on a bale or a crate he could walk past. He had nothing to leave in return. Sometimes her gang would not be there and Lang would search the harbour with his eyes for the chance of seeing her on another quay. For days they would not see each other, once for more than a week, but in the end the gangs were always close enough for a glance, a smile, that look in her eyes. They were very careful not to be noticed. Not that there was much to be noticed but, with the war getting nearer and nearer the home islands, morale was becoming a problem. There were eyes and ears everywhere, reporting to the special units of the military intelligence. It was a good time to get one's own back for past grievances.

It was late in July when they came for Lang. It was a crisp clear morning. It looked as if it was going to be hot. The prisoners were lined up on the parade ground answering the roll call. The truck came through the gates and across the compound at speed. A soldier jumped down and handed a paper to the commandant. He read it then called for Lang. The man next him pushed him forward.

"They want you, mate. You're their pal. Maybe they'll give you a medal."

Lang walked out in front of the prisoners. The old commandant had been at the camp for two years. He knew Lang was not one to give trouble but he must have been wrong about this Englishman. One of the special units wanted him at the barracks in town. It was not likely he would return to the camp. The commandant pointed to the truck and turned away. The soldier prodded with his rifle. Lang stumbled forward. He was dazed. He sensed he was being taken away for some sort of trial. Maybe just questioning. But why? He had done nothing wrong. He had obeyed the rules. He had worked as hard as he could. He was at the truck. He climbed up and was pushed the rest of the way in by the soldier who clambered up after him. The truck roared away, spurring up the dust as it turned and sped out of the gates. Lang heard the hissing and booing from the assembled prisoners. He remembered what his neighbour had said. He thought they were hissing at him.

He had to cling to the bench as the truck hurried into town over the rutted roads. The soldier hung on to the tarpaulin frame and watched him with a sort of evil satisfaction. Or was it pity? At the barracks he got down from the truck and was taken along a corridor to a small room. It was bare but for a table and a chair. He stood in front of the table. Two soldiers took up position behind him, one left, one right. He tried to look round but a rap with a rifle butt on the back of his legs turned his gaze ahead. He stood like that for half an hour. Then the door in the corner of the room opened.

The officer who came in seemed tall for a Japanese. On his head he wore the high crowned active service cap. He walked to the desk, laid down a file and flicked it open. He studied it for several minutes, tapping his boots all the time with his cane. Then he looked up and examined this prisoner.

"I am Major Kuno. Your name is Lang, John Lang. Is that correct?"

"Yes, it is. And I want to know why I've been brought here."

"To answer some questions, Lang. That's what we do here.

We ask questions and get answers." The major's English was very good. Its precision was unnatural and he still had that sibilance few Japanese could eradicate completely.

"Ask away then. I've got no answers."

"Come now, Lang. Don't disappoint me. I always get answers."

Lang said nothing.

The major peered at the papers on his desk. "It says here that you are suspected of conducting sabotage in the dock area."

"Rubbish."

Kuno smiled and walked from behind the desk to stand beside his prisoner. He looked him up and down. Yes, he decided, it might turn out to be very rewarding. Very rewarding. He walked round behind the soldiers and viewed Lang from the other side.

Lang turned his head. "I said it was rubbish. I don't know anything about any sabotage."

"Is that so?" The major walked back to the table and sat down. He laid his cane down, tip facing away from him. The tip was metal, honed to a needle sharp point. He smiled. "Yes, I know that."

John Lang stared for a few seconds. "You know that? Then why am I here?"

"Why indeed?" Kuno was warming to his task. Yes, it was going to turn out very well. Out of all these reports he had picked the one which could give him real satisfaction. He lay back in his chair and savoured it in prospect.

It had been a long and exhausting war for the major. He had been asking and getting answers for more than three years. He had been in almost every theatre of the Pacific war. His record was outstanding. But hardly ever in all that time had he been really satisfied with his art. Kuno thought of himself as an artist. Given time, he believed he could break any man

43

without harming a hair on his head. Given time, he believed he could make an innocent man really believe in his own guilt. Ordinary interrogation was a military necessity. It was his job and he did it well. Time was short so it was a crude process. There was all the beating and torturing. All the screaming and groaning. All the blood and vomit, teeth and nails. Revolting. The end justified the means. It was reasonably quick and reasonably effective. More often than not, you got the information you wanted. But that was all you got. No, not all. There was the money and the hoarded gold the civilian victims offered as bribes. That would be useful after the war. But there was never the deep personal satisfaction Kuno expected his art to give him. He had almost given up hope of finding a case to match his skill. He knew the war was coming to an end. Many of his brother officers wanted to fight on, to resist the invasion of the home islands. It was a hopeless task. He knew he would be looked for when it was all over. He had never tried to hide his identity. He felt sure he would be high on the American wanted list. So he would have to disappear, become a civilian again. He had made plans. It would not be too difficult. When he came to these barracks he knew time was very short. He prayed for a really challenging case. His instinct answered his prayers.

Out of all the informers' reports of profiteering, looting, and sabotage, his eyes settled on one that had all the marks of spiteful tittle-tattle about it. It said that a woman working on the docks was giving herself to one of the seamen prisoners who worked there too. He made inquiries. It was a malicious story. But the truth was far more intriguing. He had the man identified. Then he asked the prison camp for a report. He made a note to commend the old camp commandant. The report was full. John Lang obeyed all the rules to the letter. He was not popular with the other prisoners. He kept to himself. He objected to bawdy stories and foul language. He was strong willed enough to live through a long confinement without the company of his fellows. A lamb for the slaughter, thought Kuno. A remarkable people, the English. Here was this man, strong willed, well disciplined, pure in heart and mind; and he had been ogling a Japanese woman of low class from a distance for months. Very poetic. Kuno understood. He wrote poetry himself.

Lang was up at the table, shouting. "Don't just sit there, damn you. Tell me. Why am I here?" The two soldiers grabbed him and pulled him back.

The major shook his head. "Patience, my dear fellow. All in good time. You must not do anything like that. These chaps are rather primitive. They might hurt you if they think you are insulting me or trying to attack me." He signed to the soldiers to let Lang go. "There now. You are quite right, of course. I should have explained. The mention of suspected sabotage on these papers is just for the record, as you say. Just for the record."

Lang stood up straight. "I still don't know why I'm here."

"You will, Lang." Kuno leaned across the table. "You are here to help me with a morale problem we have with the civilian population."

John Lang shook his head.

"Yes, I think you can help me, Lang. This is the problem. Some of our people here are very upset that one of our local women has been, how do you put it, playing about with one of the prisoners from your camp." Kuno watched his prisoner's face. He saw bewilderment, then disbelief, then fear, maybe a trace of guilt. "Tell me what you know, Lang."

"I don't know what you're talking about."

"Come, come. Just tell me. I am a man of the world. I will understand. You have been a prisoner here for three years, more than that. I am not going to blame you for taking what pleasure you can."

45

"I tell you I don't know what you're talking about."

"I can understand that you do not want to talk about it. Nothing will happen to you. We have this problem of morale. We just want to know the facts. We have the woman's side of the story. Now we want to hear your side."

"Don't you dare lay a finger on her." Lang's step forward was checked by the major's pointed cane.

"That is better. Now we are getting at the truth. You admit there was a woman. You admit that you are the man. Or were there several men?"

"There was nothing."

"Come, come, Lang. You have admitted there was something between you and this woman."

"There was nothing. You must believe me, Major. You mustn't harm her. We just watched each other. I looked at her. She looked at me. We were never near enough to touch."

Kuno looked sceptical.

"It's true, damn you. I've never been with a woman in my whole life."

The major smiled and nodded. He congratulated himself. I was right. All my surmise was right. Very gratifying. "That seems unlikely, Lang. You are now thirty-six years of age. By profession you are a seaman. You want me to believe you are a virgin?"

Lang felt his face flushing. "I'm not ashamed of that."

"Good for you, my dear fellow. I understand, of course. I am an educated man. What worries me now is what your thoughts about this woman must have been. You must know from your wonderful Christian literature that you can be as much an adulterer in thought as in practice. You would be an adulterer, Lang. That woman is married to a Japanese soldier in Malaya."

"Shut up, will you. What d'you want with me. You couldn't

ever understand what my thoughts are. Do whatever you want to do and get it over with."

"No, no, Lang. You have it all upside down. All I want is the truth. Now, you say you never touched this woman. She has said that you did. Frequently. She did not suggest that you forced yourself on her. She admitted she was willing. Who is telling the truth? That is all I want to know."

"I don't believe she ever said these things."

Kuno shook his head. "Unfortunately, Lang, you have to take my word for what she said. She is not here now, if you see what I mean."

Lang's leap at the major was held by the guards. Kuno was pleased. He really was going to enjoy himself It took him a long time but, in the end, he was satisfied with his first day's work. Lang was convinced the woman had been butchered. He was convinced it had happened because of him. All his denials, all the abuse he roared at the major, were turned back against him. All his loathing for his own father came out. The major picked it up and was sympathetic about the inevitability of heredity. He kept telling Lang he did not hold him responsible. He just wanted to get at the whole truth. But Lang knew who was responsible. He felt he was responsible. At one point he even conceded that the major had had no choice in what he had done to the woman. There were rules. There was a war. Kuno found he had to say so little. It was stimulating to deal with someone with imagination. Say one word and Lang's tortured conscience would grab at it and turn it against himself. What pleased the major most of all as he goaded Lang towards disintegration was the thought of that woman working happily down at the docks, maybe just wondering for a moment or two where her prisoner was.

It was evening when the major called a halt. Lang had been standing all day. He was being held up by two soldiers. He had not been beaten or tortured but he was exhausted and his mind was a frantic jumble. He was still cursing Kuno for harming the woman and cursing himself for having caused it. Kuno had him put in a punishment pit out on the parade ground. He felt Lang was a resilient character. It would be interesting to take him out in the morning and see what a night alone had done for him. Kuno was cheated of that pleasure by the stick of bombs that took out the barracks that night. They found no trace of his body in the debris. He was presumed killed.

The major had been right about Lang's resilience. Lang was dedicated above all things to his own survival. At the bottom of that ten foot pit, that thought persisted in his tormented mind. It was dark. It was slimy. He felt the slime on his hands and on his legs. He felt it as the woman's blood, that woman he thought he had sent to a dreadful death. He screamed and roared, he beat at the earth walls. The earth was hard-packed, but a tiny piece broke loose and the dry soft earth behind cascaded over his hands. It made a small sound as it trickled away. That gave him his escape. In a frenzy he clawed at the walls. He clawed at them and scraped at them. He struck them to break through to the earth behind. His nails splintered and were torn off. The flesh was scratched and scraped from his fingers. He felt nothing. He wanted that earth. Lots of it. He was going to bury that imagined corpse beneath him. He was going to bury it deep and with it he was going to bury his memory of Kuno and the woman and his own terrible guilt. John Lang was going to survive.

He survived but so did his memories and his guilt. They found him late the next afternoon when they were clearing away the debris of the barracks. One of the workers pulled away the cover of the pit and saw the man down at the bottom. He was unconscious. There was no one there who knew that the pit had been two feet deeper the day before. When they saw his fingers, they shook their heads. The police had some terrible tortures. They could see he was a European. He must have come from the prison camp. They sent him back there.

At the camp they did what they could for his fingers. The doubters decided they had been wrong about him. When he came to, he said nothing. A few more days and the war was over. The Americans came. There was food and drugs and vitamins and cigarettes. No one had to worry. The Yanks were there and soon everyone would be all right again. In the camp office they put together John Lang's story. They found Kuno's summons. It said there was undeniable evidence that Lang had been engaged in sabotage in the docks. He was in pretty bad shape. They asked no questions. It was all written into the record. The prisoners were shipped to America, fêted, made well, sent home. The records followed and John Lang got his medal. Sometimes he almost believed he had earned it the way the citation said. Most of the time it was a goad to his guilt.

Lang sat in his chair, staring at his claw-like fingers. No, he could not forget about Kim Odinoku because she reminded him of that other woman he had sent to a grisly death. No, he could not forget about Mr. Yashawa. Or was it Major Kuno? They had never found the major's body. He had been presumed dead. Presumed. Lang had accepted that till he came back to Japan. Then, gradually, the evidence mounted. No one knew anything about Mr. Yashawa before he came to Shinoto after the war. But they knew he was tall for a Japanese. They knew that he was suddenly taken ill just before the crew came out to join the *Emperor*. He could no longer get about. He had to stay up there in his penthouse on top of the hotel. No, there were no photos of him. No, he never saw visitors.

Lang shook his head. That's not evidence. But it's suspicion and it's stuck deep down inside me. I've got to know for sure.

What if he is Kuno? What can I do now? What good can it do? One way or the other, maybe it will give me some peace, I've got to know for sure. There's not much time. Just tomorrow. I've got to know. Somehow I've got to get up there into that penthouse and see for myself.

CHAPTER FOUR

The tyres squealed and the soft suspension subsided as the car took the bend. The Japanese driver grinned happily. It was not often he had the chance to take the big car for a real run. The crowded streets of Tokyo and Yokohama were frustrating to anyone who knew about all these litres under the bonnet. Eugene North noticed nothing. He spent a large part of his life being driven by other people. Rome, Naples, Paris, Frankfurt, London, New York. He had long since developed the habit of ignoring cars and drivers and getting on with his work.

Not so his wife. Sonia had been through the thrill-girl stage; she was now a comfort-woman. "Gene, must we go so fast?"

"Hmm?"

"The car, darling. It's like we're at Indianapolis. I want to see the scenery. Can we slow down?"

Her husband looked up. "Yes, I suppose so. If you like. Victor, tell the man to ease up a bit."

"Yes, sir." Victor Grosset was in the front seat. He tapped the driver on the shoulder and signed to him to slow down. The Japanese pretended not to understand at first but then reluctantly lifted his foot off the throttle. These VIP's were all the same, spoilsports.

As the car slowed down to a more sedate pace, Sonia settled

back in her seat and took a cigarette from her bag. Grosset was ready with a lighter. "Thank you, Vic. Now tell me all about Japan."

Grosset had done his homework. He was good at public relations. He had some success at private relations too. He had his own interpretation of the dictum that, in business, executive wives were important. He had found they provided an influential route to their husbands' ears. Sonia North was a very important executive wife. Victor sat next the driver, twisted round over the back of the seat, giving Sonia a running commentary on the countryside between Tokyo International Airport and Shinoto. He had had the Yashawa plane standing by at the airport but was pleased that North had decided to make the journey by car. This way Victor had more time.

He hardly ever thought about his antecedents. When he did he was sure that Grandfather Grosse would have approved of his progress. Victor's grandfather had come to England from Germany before the First World War. The "t" was added to the family name in 1914. The Grossets were tailors. Victor's grandfather had worked at first in the sweat shops of London's East End. By the time the war came and he changed his name, he was in business in a small way on his own account. By the end of the war there was money in the bank. That was just as well for business was never again so brisk. But the Grossets lived well, they were middle class, they had to be careful but they always had enough to eat which was more than could be said for a lot of people between the wars. Victor was five when the Second World War started. He never worried much about the Blitz. It was a thrill for a small boy to spend his nights in tube stations. There was a bit more money again from the uniform contracts for the forces. Not a fortune but enough to buy Victor a grammar school place when it was all over. He had a flair for wearing clothes but none at all for making them. His talent lay in his looks and his fluent tongue. After school he started in an advertising agency. Clients liked him. He had nice manners and a quickness at grasping what people wanted. It was after working on a promotion for Inoco that he got the offer of a job in its publicity department. From that chance beginning he had built himself up. He was incapable of really original thought but he was adept at picking other people's brains and blending all these random ideas into the right kind of package. Now he had his chance. He was responsible for the PR work on Project Emperor. For the British end anyway. It was a big idea; it was his big chance. He was doing well. Victor Grosset was starting to be noticed. There was a rumour that Eugene North might be looking for a personal assistant. That was Victor's kind of job. He did not fancy the strain and exposure of being right at the top; Victor was at his best close behind the throne. He kept talking.

Sonia listened and watched the countryside sailing past the window. It was a disappointment. She had never been in Japan. She had expected lots of people all dressed up like Madame Butterfly with Mount Fuji rearing up in the background. It was not like that at all. She nodded idly as Grosset told his story and asked questions at the right moments. Sonia was good at this. She had learned her social life at business conferences and cocktail parties. She was more astute than most people gave her credit for. She had already weighed up Victor. Nice, pleasant boy. Ambitious but doesn't have what it takes. She was North's third wife; she had been his secretary before that. They had been married less than a year. She had no intention of going the way of the other two wives. She liked Gene a lot. She admired him. Maybe she loved him. That would depend on what definition was used. But she intended to keep him. He worked hard. His main interest was Inoco. That was admirable for he did not need to work. He was wealthy. He just liked working; it was not for money or for power, just for achievement. There was a lot of satisfaction in seeing a man achieve something. There were other compensations too, when you were married to him and he was a millionaire.

She dropped her cigarette in the ashtray and snapped it shut. She snuggled back into the cushions. Grosset got the message. He stopped his commentary and turned to watch the road ahead. Sonia smiled. Full marks, Vic. She took a compact from her bag and studied her face in the mirror. Not bad considering we spent most of the night in that jet. She etched in her lipstick. She was a fine looking woman, into her thirties now, handsome rather than pretty. There was a quiet assurance about her that appealed. She snapped shut the compact and watched her husband. He made no sign. Might have known. When Gene's doing his prep, as he calls it, it takes more than a snapping compact and a puff of expensive powder to disturb him.

Gene North was doing his prep. He was a methodical man. He felt he had to be. He was always trying to be what he was purely for his worth and not because of his family connections. "I have to do my prep." It was one of his favourite phrases. It was revealing. He had picked it up in England where homework was set in ordinary schools; in the public schools, that is to say, the private schools, it was called prep. Eugene North was an Anglophile. That was not uncommon among the American aristocracy; he just took it to greater lengths than most. If he had had a son, he would have been sent to public school in England. Gene had all the respect for long traditions so dear to those without any. He had all his suits made in London. His hats, his gloves, his umbrellas. His garages held British cars. His yacht, which he never sailed himself, was built on the Clyde. His great ambition had been to head Inoco's European operations. That he had now achieved. He was now launched on making Britain and Europe as big a part of the Inoco business as was America.

53

He had come into the company because the Norths owned a successful family business with the right leases on the right ground at the right time. North Oil stood in the way of the new Inoco. So North Oil became a part of Inoco, Eugene's father joined the board, and Eugene got a chance to prove himself. He had worked hard at it. He was not now one of the top men because of the value of his father's founder shares. There were members of the other original families without any executive say. Gene North was there because he was the best man and doing his prep was how he intended to keep it that way.

He closed the folder and let it drop into his lap. He caught sight of Grosset's anxious face in the driving mirror. No, not now, Victor. I can't be bothered telling you you've done a good job. Why should you expect that anyway? That's what you're paid for. So you have done a good job arranging for all the free advertising and the party and the launching and the catering on the trials. You have brought along notes and photos of everyone I have to meet, so that I can appear to know them all like long lost brothers. So what? That's just hack work. Sonia did all that for me when she was my secretary. She never expected constant congratulation. Gene closed his eyes to shut off the sight of Grosset. It's nice Sonia's here this time. I should take her along more often. He could smell her perfume close by. I must do that. Oh, I'm tired. Only dozed in that plane last night. I won't sleep though. Not now, not with Project Emperor really about to start. No, I won't sleep but I'll lie back here with my eyes closed and savour it all. And worry about it. Of course I'll worry about it. It's the biggest capital programme in the company's history. But it's worry with satisfaction. The kind of worry that tones up tired brains, not the kind that grows ulcers. It's worry about scale and imagination and originality. Healthy worry. Gene North was in his early fifties and toning up his mind and body was of constant concern to him. For his body he made do with one session each week at a health club and exercises every morning before breakfast; for his mind he was always looking for a new challenge.

This one had started almost four years before. It had started as a report to the New York Head Office from the company's new, young Director of Marine Operations in London. North had been impressed. It was not just a report that commented on the fleet operations and looked ahead for a year or two. It was a careful survey of the whole field of oil transportation, with particular reference to shipping. It probed deep into the future, decades rather than years. It had a freshness about it, a confidence, an air of radical thinking. It was a stimulating document. Many who read it paid lip service to its advanced thought but were quick to write it off as a transparent attempt by a go-getter to get there by a short cut. Gene North had no cause to be scathing. On his next trip to London he made a point of meeting James Bruce. Project Emperor was born that day.

At first it was a very vague scheme. It recognised certain facts. That crude oil from Libya and the Sahara was flooding into Europe in increasing quantities. That this oil was cheap because transport costs were low. That Inoco had no stake in these fields. That Inoco's major source of crude was in the Persian Gulf. That Inoco wanted to extend its business in Europe and wanted to do it by refining and selling its own crude. The problem was how to get the Persian Gulf crude to the European refineries at a really competitive price. At that time the company's ships varied in size from small coasters up to supertankers of 50,000 tons. Ships of 90,000 tons were building. There was talk of even bigger ones being planned in Japan and elsewhere. Maybe these ships could be chartered by Inoco. The result of that first meeting was that North gave Bruce permission to establish the research unit he wanted. He had already caused a stir by instituting surveys in the ships of the fleet. Now he was to have the means of interpreting the results, getting better results and making plans. North had had the job, and it was not easy, of justifying his sanction to the doubters in London and New York. He got limited agreement. He was satisfied with that. He was confident that Bruce would cast his net wide and come up with a bumper catch.

It had been a running battle the whole way, with James Bruce interpreting his role with a fine disregard for the accepted holy writ within Inoco and his detractors desperately trying to block each new move after it had been made. North had been the umpire, biased in favour of his protégé but never being seen to be unfair. He had enjoyed it all. It let him tighten the reins on Bruce now and again. That was necessary. It maybe reflected in a small way Gene's disappointment that his protégé was not the kind of Englishman he admired. He was not English. He was a Scot. No, he was not really that either. He was a man who truly saw the world as his oyster. But because of that he was headstrong, maybe cocksure. North found that forcing little compromises on him disciplined him best. Little compromises like that business with the commodore, what was his name, Lang, yes, that was it, Commodore Lang. Of course, Jim Bruce soon wriggled out of that. But it kept the game going.

The Research Unit had taken a long, cold, hard and extraordinarily detailed look at Inoco's problems. It had not stopped at transportation. It had ranged far. It took a year to produce a result but that result was, in all but a few insignificant details, the basis of what was now known as Project Emperor.

When the report first exploded on Inoco there was a shocked silence then the wailing started. People who saw their own carefully constructed empires in jeopardy quickly banded together to quell the revolution. But it was already too late. North brought Bruce over to New York when decision making was imminent. In a two week marathon he took committee after committee by storm; no ranting, no raving, no hard selling— just hard facts, lots of them, and a pungent wit. The core of the project was the idea of leaping ahead to a tanker size of half a million tons. To those who doubted that it was possible from an engineering point of view, he replied with a full design study, a costing, and an agreement from a yard to build. To those who queried the economics, he came back with a careful and conservative breakdown showing that the ship would carry more than five times the cargo for a capital cost of only three times that of existing tankers, and it would ship oil at less than half the cost per ton. To those who argued that all existing refineries would become useless because they were sited near water too shallow to float the new mammoth, he showed that several refineries could be served by offshore pipelines from new single point mooring sites. In Britain, one new vast storage dump in the south west corner of Scotland could feed supplies by smaller ship and pipeline to the existing plants. To those who complained that the whole thing was too radical, too big to attempt in one operation, he replied caustically that radicalism was not a sin. Radicalism was what made money. And he went on to list what the Research Unit had already achieved. It had cost them nothing though they had all fought against its establishment. It was making money. Much that it had learned was already being bought by other companies. The new technique of steel preparation and protection looked like making a fortune for Inoco Paints & Plastics. The new systems of training and selection could be used to set up an Administrative College to keep Inoco in the forefront of management technique. Its services could be sold. It could bring a flow of top class managers under the eye of the company to pick and choose from other industries' top brains. The new ideas on automation at sea had already produced interest from manufacturers. The new tank cleaning and sludge disposal systems had attracted oil companies and governments. Studies of pipe-line techniques had brought requests from companies outside the oil business. Diversification—it was the accountants' own weapon turned against them. Then back to the core of the problem. The new ship. Its economics depended on scrapping established manning schemes. Would the unions agree? Bruce said he was assured they would. He proved it. To do so he bent the facts. In the event this was almost to be his downfall but the '66 seamen's strike happened providentially. It left behind it uncertainty. Where Bruce had wheedled, now he roared. He got his breakthrough.

But before all that, he had won New York to his plan. There were cutbacks here and there, unimportant but face saving. In essence, Project Emperor got the green light. And with it James Bruce moved ahead. He was now Managing Director of Inoco Transportation (UK) with a seat on the boards of Inoco (UK) and the European holding company. Good going for an ex-captain. Eugene North kept a close eye on him. Gene intended to have at least another ten years at the top. He was not going to be swallowed by his own offspring. But he enjoyed it all. Jim Bruce was a stimulating man to work with. There was no end to his ingenuity in advancing himself. No small detail was overlooked. As now, with the new ship about to be launched. The biggest ship in the world, a ship that would never have been built without his vision. But Bruce was not going to be there. Maybe he was too busy planning a million ton ship, or a submarine tanker, or a nuclear powered vessel, or one of these ships with only a bow and a stern and portable cargo tanks in between to be unlocked and floated out and thus cut the port time from hours to minutes. These were only some of the Research Unit's ideas. But the real reason that Bruce was not going to be in Shinoto tomorrow was that he would be more obvious by his absence.

Gene smiled as he lay back in the car, eyes closed. He always smiled when he thought of Jim. They got on well together. They understood each other. Gene was not really worried about Bruce superseding him, for Bruce had one weakness. He had no money of his own. You needed money of your own or power over other people's money to make it to the top and stay there. North's holding in Inoco and the rest of his wealth was his ace in the hole.

"We're almost there, sir." It was Grosset.

North opened his eyes and grunted.

Sonia was sitting forward in her seat, peering ahead. "It looks just like any other town. Quite picturesque with that hill and the sea beyond, I suppose."

"What did you expect, darling?"

"Oh, I don't know. Something Japanese. Like the travel brochures."

"That's the hotel," said Grosset, pointing.

"Oh. Well, that's a bit Japanese, isn't it. It's got that temple place on top of it."

"That's where old Mr. Yashawa lives."

"In the temple? Hmm. Quite nice. Who's Mr. Yashawa?"

"He owns the hotel. He owns everything here. The shipyard, the factories, the whole town."

"He sounds better off than you, Gene," said Sonia.

"I dare say. Don't leave me for him, will you, dear."

She put out her hand. "I won't. I didn't marry you for your money, darling." They smiled at each other. It was a private joke.

Grosset kept his eyes to the front.

The car drew into the entrance plaza and the hotel manager opened the door and bowed and hissed his greetings. The foyer was littered with equipment and busy with staff arranging flowers and arguing about the arrangements for the party that evening. When the manager and the porters and the maids

59

had left, Sonia kicked off her shoes and padded round the suite.

"I suppose it's all right."

"What's the matter now?" asked Gene.

"You know, it's like everything else. It could be New York. Or anywhere."

Her husband smiled. He liked that ingenuous streak in her.

"I mean, where are all the parchment walls and miniature dressing tables and everything?"

"I'll ask the manager."

"Don't bother. It's not for long." She was at the window of their sitting-room. The view was right out over the town and the shipyard to the sea. "Is that it?"

"What now?" He came over and stood beside her.

"The ship. This famous ship. Is that it down there?"

"I suppose so. God but it's big. I hadn't realised."

"It's big all right," said Sonia, "but it's just like a huge barge. Where do we stay? What do we do for two weeks across to California?"

"Now, Sonia, you're getting bitchy. You wait till you see inside it. You'll be surprised. You'll enjoy the trip."

She took his hand and tucked it under her arm. "I know, Gene." She smiled. "Sorry if I sounded bad tempered. I must be tired after that plane trip. Whatever it's like it will be worth it to be with you for all that time. No office, no telephone, just us."

He bent down and kissed her. "That's my girl."

She went through and plumped down on one of the beds. "This is good," she called. "Can I go to bed now or do we have to start shaking hands right away?"

"You can sleep, my dear. Nothing happens till this afternoon. We have to tour the shipyard then."

"Good. I'll catch up on my sleep." She started taking off

60

her clothes. "Ask them to call me, darling, when the *suki-yaki* or the raw fish or whatever they have for lunch is ready." She got into bed and pulled the covers round her. "I suppose it'll turn out to be hamburgers and hashed potatoes."

CHAPTER FIVE

It was quite unreal. Eugene North sat in the swing chair in front of the curved console with its dials and screens and re-peaters and banks of switches and levers. The newness, the unreality had not been so obvious on board the ship. Thinking back on it he realised that the navigating bridge of the *Emperor* had not been like any bridge he had ever seen before. There was a control console like this one, placed high up at the after end of the wheelhouse, four or five feet above the level of the walkway across the bridgefront. A sort of split-level bridge. And all round, 360 degrees, at console height was armoured glass window. But it had all been on top of a superstructure in the middle of a ship. That had preserved a semblance of normality. Now, here in the training shed, it seemed more mysterious, unlikely, wholly foreign. He was sure he could smell the lingering scent of fish. He wished Stock had not told him that the shed had once been a fish cannery.

He had come down to the yard after lunch with Sonia. They were given the red carpet treatment, shaking hands and being bowed and hissed at in the Japanese way. They saw through the offices and the prefabrication sheds and the engine works. They had a quick look round the ship itself and met again the officers and crew men they had been introduced to at the hotel. Grosset had arranged for Sonia to appear in one

61

or two scenes of the film they were making of the new ship from keel laying to launch, so she stayed on board with the film team and Commodore Lang while Gene came over with Stock to see the training shed. Funny thing about that commodore, thought North. Good job I had my notes on him. Can't remember ever meeting him before. Nice old chap though; a bit hot under the collar at having the boss and his wife on board. Or maybe he was worried about being filmed. Or maybe Jim Bruce was right all along; maybe he was worried about this new ship. Can't say I blame him. This is not for oldsters. He looked round at the maze of controls. It's like a TV studio.

"Come on then, Captain. I suppose you want to show me this box of tricks."

"It'll be a pleasure, Gene. We're quite proud of this lot." Stock moved over to a smaller console and set some switches.

North breathed hard. Sometimes I wonder about all this familiarity. I must be getting old. I don't like being called by my first name by this chap. Yes, of course, I told him to call me that. Why do these young ones take me at my word? Lang doesn't. He says, "Yes, sir," and goes on calling me Mr. North. But I'll give Stock his due. It's only when we're alone. He stared. In front of his eyes the sea had magically appeared where before there had only been a white wall. "That's a neat trick, Captain."

Stock pulled up a chair beside him. "It is, isn't it. It's a back projection screen. We can feed in any kind of traffic situation we want. The view is as near as we could get to what the officer of the watch will see when he's sitting at the command console and looking through the windows."

North shook his head. "It certainly is realistic. I could get sea sick watching that."

"Please don't. That's about the only thing we haven't planned for. If you throw up over this lot all the circuits will probably blow. Now let's see what's happening." Stock leaned over and moved his hands over the console, flicking switches. "There you are now. We're at sea." He pointed and explained. "Speed through the water is sixteen knots. That's the course. We're running down through the Gulf of Oman towards Ras al Hadd. D'you know the area? It's when you're coming from the Persian Gulf, just before you hit the Arabian Sea. Ras al Hadd's where the locals once ate the lighthouse keepers for dinner. There, you see it on the chart there. That's new. That's a development of the flight log system they use on aircraft. We've got old-fashioned charts too, of course. We'll use them for ocean passages like this first one across the Pacific but the idea is that in close waters, near coasts, we use this automatic recorder. The chart is fed in and lined up under this window here. There are two pens. One is controlled by the course and speed the ship is set on, the other is locked to the signals from the shore radio beacons. So we always know where we should be and we always know exactly where we really are. There, you see, the chart's moving up under the window now and we can see the actual coastline along to the corner at Hadd."

"What's the red line on the chart? Some sort of danger?"

"Right first time. These charts are specially made. These ships draw the best part of a hundred feet of water fully laden so we can't risk paddling in the shallows. That red line marks the twenty fathom limit below which we might be in trouble. The ink's a magnetic type. If we stray too near it, one of these alarms blows and goes on blowing till the course has been corrected."

"Very clever."

"Look there on the radar screen. You can see the whole coastline now just as on the chart. There's a target just showing clear of the point. Look ahead. No, up ahead through the windows. See it, that's the Hadd and there's the tanker just starting to make its turn into the Gulf."

"I see."

"Now watch. I've got the advantage of you here. I've seen this one before. That tanker's a corner cutter. He's going to squeeze us in towards the danger mark. Watch the radar. It's on true motion display. Watch his afterglow. See, it's a near collision course. Obvious thing to do is for us to come to starboard. O.K. Pull her to starboard. There, that's fine. Angle's opening up. But watch. He's come to port again round the point. We're squeezed again. More starboard you say. All right, more starboard. There we are. Now listen and watch that chart."

The green stylus on the chart traced the ship towards the red danger line. Wheeee! "Good God," gasped North as the alarm blew.

"Naughty Mr. Officer-of-the-Watch," said Stock. "Can't do that. Hard-a-port, cross his course, get north of him and give yourself room." He spun the rudder control. "There now, that's better. Watch the radar. Watch the chart. Watch out the window." They waited as all the views changed. "There you are, Gene. Back to normal again." Mike pulled the main switch and everything went blank. "Very short trip but it gives you some idea."

North closed his eyes then opened them. "Thanks, Captain. I'm suitably impressed. It's like some sort of dream."

"It is a dream. A dream come true. Jim Bruce's dream."

"That's a fact. You know, Mike, I've been in on this project right from the start. I've read I don't know how many memos about it, but I didn't know what to expect. Not this. This is just like one of the refineries. One man, sitting pressing buttons, and keeping a whole cracking plant going."

"That's a fair comparison."

"But this isn't a refinery. This is a ship."

"So what?"

"Isn't a ship different? It's mobile, it could be lethal."

64

"So could a refinery; it would make a beautiful big bang."

"Of course, but it still seems different. This is really a big step forward to an automatic ship."

"Didn't Jim tell you?"

"Of course he did. But somehow that seemed just part of the sales talk. It was a big ship but it was being built in a ship-yard like any other ship. It had men on board. It's only seeing it, seeing this box of tricks, that makes it all suddenly real."

"It's real enough. What you see here is what you'll see when the *Emperor*'s at sea. But the ultimate dream is a long way off. We've got the technology. There are other things. There are men, and unions, and companies, and other ships, and governments. But this is a start."

North nodded slowly. "Men. You mention men. That's a point. What happens to a man sitting in this seat for four hours? What happens if he goes to sleep, or gets ill?"

"Do us a favour, Gene. We've thought of all that. We've got a whole series of built-in checks. And remember there will always be two officers on duty up here; one at the console, the other down on the bridgefront. After all, this may be new on ships but men have been doing this sort of thing for years on aircraft."

"I suppose that's true."

"Then there's the closed circuit TV between here and the engine control centre. That's another check. The officers there and up here have to check on each other all the time. Watch." Stock snapped a switch. "Hallo, engine room."

A face formed on one of the screens. It spoke to them. "Hallo, Mike. Oh, hallo, Mr. North. You getting indoctrinated?"

"It seems like it."

"That's George Moffat," explained Stock. "The chief engineer."

65

"I know who it is. Hello there, Chief. This is quite something, isn't it?"

"It's not bad for a bridge. They're a bit cocky because they can control the engines from up there. But if you want to see something that's really something, come along here to my end of the shed."

"I'll maybe do that if I can catch my breath in time."

"I'll be here."

The screen went blank as Stock switched off. "The old oil and water rivalry's still there, you see. But it's all very friendly nowadays. That's another thing about this ship. The old departments are all mixed up together. It's becoming difficult to tell an engineer from a navigator. Jim Bruce says that soon there'll be no difference. There'll just be shipmen, and they'll have to be able to do everything."

"Another dream?"

"Of course but it'll come true. It's already started. Look at this set-up here. A complete computer-controlled simulator for training the officers and men. Inoco built it. Inoco runs it. Gone are the days when a man got a Master's ticket in his middle twenties then burned his books and went on adding stripes on his cuff while his brain addled. Now we start with them *after* their Master's tickets. We send them to Castle Brainwash, then we bring them out here. We train them to be a new kind of sailor. And we go on training them. For ever. When they get to the stage where they can't take re-training, we'll have to get rid of them."

"You make it sound pretty inhuman, Captain."

"Maybe. Progress can be tough. You know that. It's happening ashore in business. Why not at sea?"

"No reason, I suppose." North shook his head and stood up. "At my age, Captain, you hate to admit even to yourself that you may be in the expendable bracket."

"Nothing personal, sir."

66

North grinned. "O.K., Mike. Is there anything else to see here?"

"The best is yet to come. Down below." Stock led the way to the stairway. "Down here is the operations room." They clattered down the wooden staircase. The room held two control consoles both quite different in appearance from the one on the bridge. "I don't know if you remember from the ship but, on board, this room is directly under the after end of the bridge. From here we can control all the loading and discharging, ballasting and tank cleaning. It's all automatic. You know how on the old system you had to run around twisting valves and starting pumps and peering down into tanks and dipping and ullaging. That's all finished now. Want a demonstration?"

"Why not?"

"Good man. Take a pew." Stock walked round the room setting switches. "Now, you see that illuminated panel there in front of you. That's a complete tank and pipeline diagram. It works something like these boards in a new railway signal box. You select the route you want the oil to take, loading or discharging, then you set the switches for all the valves and these indicators show if they're open or shut. Then if you're loading, you open the gate valve to the shore; if you're discharging, you start the pumps then open the gate valve. If anything goes wrong, it shows up either on the indicators or the dials. D'you follow me so far?"

"Sort of. But go on."

"Well, say you're loading 3, 5, 7 and 9 tanks across. You know what level you want the oil to come to in each tank so you set that level on each tank dial. You then set the controls for the next set of tanks you want to fill. When the first lot reach the right level, they cut off and start filling the second set. And so on till you're loaded. All the time you can tell how the ship is lying in the water, draught and trim. Here you get exact readings of the cargo temperature. With that and the ullage, the trim and the API figures the shore boys supply, you can spin up this calculator and tell exactly how much cargo's on board."

"Tell me, what if all this automatic equipment fails?"

"Shoosh. You mustn't even mention the possibility. But that's not really a problem. Everything's arranged for old-fashioned manual control. If it's ever needed the only problem will be whether the men on board have enough muscle to spin valves."

"Don't tell me Jim Bruce didn't think of that."

"He did. To stay in this crew you've got to be 100 A1 at Lloyd's. He even thought of the dangers of men sitting down all the time. All these seats are specially designed to stop you getting corns on your arse."

Eugene laughed. "That must be a real comfort. I suppose I have to ask about that other control panel over there."

"Ah, now that's really something. Tank washing unit. Come and have a look." They moved across the room. "This is worth its weight in gold. Literally. The yard here has already bought a licence to build this. Every tanker worthy of the name will have it soon. It's a Research Unit design."

"So what does it do?"

"It cleans tanks. You know the trouble there's been since these oil pollution agreements were ratified. Ships having to go way off course to dump their tank cleanings; ships having to stay in port cleaning tanks into a shore installation; ships having to clean tanks at sea into a slop tank then pumping out the slops ashore before loading could start. All that time meant money, Gene. Now that's all over. And all the labour's finished too. No more guddling about the decks lowering washing machines down the tanks, starting them up, lowering them a bit farther, then stopping and hauling them up and changing them over to another part of the tank. No creeping about tank bottoms digging out sludge by hand either. With this, one man sits here and does the lot. It's super-efficient. The washlines

68

are all built into the ship and this panel switches on the wash-water where and when you want it, at the level you want it, at the temperature and pressure you want it. The pumps suck the washings away into this permanent slop tank down aft. From there they go through a separator unit. The clean water is discharged overboard and the sludge is rammed into disposable bags. They can be dumped in deep water or landed ashore. The ship doesn't stop for a minute."

"All right, Mike, I'm overwhelmed. You wouldn't have a drink anywhere round here, would you?"

"I think we could find something down in the lecture room."

"Just a drink. No lectures. I'm surfeited."

"It's a deal."

Stock found a bottle of whisky in a cupboard. He poured two glasses and splashed in water. "It's the local brew but it's not at all bad."

North took a sip and rolled it round his mouth before swallowing. "As you say, not bad." He took a proper swallow then lit a cigarette. He sat for several minutes, nursing his glass, smoking, looking round the lecture hall with its wall charts and models and roll-over blackboard, glancing at Mike Stock, letting all the newness settle down in his mind. He had seen automated equipment in plants all over the world. He had never expected to see this degree of automation on board ship. He supposed that was because he seldom visited ships and still thought of them as something changeless in a changing world. But as he thought back he remembered hearing about all these new developments, one at a time, as Project Emperor had taken shape. He had taken little real interest in the new ship because there were plenty of other bits of the project needing his attention; and because the ship was very much Jim's own responsibility and Gene North trusted Bruce. Now he was glad he had decided to come and see the ship, and have Sonia launch it, and travel on it on its first voyage across the

Pacific to California. North was an enthusiast. He liked having something to be excited about. He had that feeling now, that tingle that seemed to tone up mind and body. He was excited about the *Emperor*.

He drained his glass and let Stock fill it up again. "You're really proud of this ship, Mike, aren't you?"

"Of course. We all are. Any man would give his eye teeth for a chance like this."

"The extra money and the extra holidays would explain that."

"Don't you believe it, Gene. I'd have taken this one for no extra." He grinned. "But don't quote me on that."

"I never heard you." North took a sip of his whisky. "But you're not typical, are you? You agreed to come here as Staff Captain. In a way that was demotion."

"What's in a name? Anyway, you're forgetting that I'm the first Staff Captain the company's ever had."

"That's true, I suppose. Are you sure everyone's as excited as you about the ship?"

"I told you, yes."

"What about the commodore?"

"What about him? He maybe thinks it's all a bit new fangled but he likes it all right. He's as proud as hell. He fought hard enough to get it."

"Did he? Did he fight for the ship or just for the right to command it?"

"It's the same difference."

"I wonder if it is, Mike. He seemed a bit strung up to me this afternoon."

"That's nothing. I'm strung up. We're all strung up. Who wouldn't be strung up the day before taking a great monster like that out there to sea for the first time? If you're worried about old Lang, forget it. He's may be a bit long in the tooth but he's tough. And he's capable. He's had to go through the

70

same training as everyone else. It must have been hard for him. But he made it."

"You surprise me, Mike. I had the impression that you didn't get along too well, you two. Now you're singing his praises."

"Why shouldn't I? He's not a bad old stick. He's a bit of a puritan, of course. I dare say there's a lot about me he doesn't like. But our only contact's professional. For my money he's a good shipmaster."

"I'm glad to hear that. If I judge you right, that's an honest opinion, not just one for the boss."

Stock looked him straight in the eyes. "You don't know me at all, Mr. North." He was still on his first drink. He took a sip. "You should tell whoever does your confidential reports to dig a little deeper. I only ever have one opinion about anything. It doesn't change with the wind. What you don't know about me is that I've got an ace up my sleeve in this get-to-the-top game."

North was intrigued. This unlikely looking sea captain was full of surprises. "Am I to be let into the secret?"

"Why not? You see, I've got no ambition."

"That's interesting. How old are you, Mike?"

"Thirty-six."

"Thirty-six, eh. And no ambition. You can afford to make that claim. You're already a captain, have been for six years, and now you're one of the most important men in this whole project."

"That means nothing. That's just how it happened. I'm pleased it happened. I like what I'm doing. I like what I'll be doing for the rest of my life. But that's not ambition. No, ambitious people don't just let things happen. They daren't. They plot, they plan, they clamber up the ladder over other ambitious people. You know, the corridors of power and all that. I suppose you're ambitious; you're up there at the top.

71

Jim Bruce is ambitious. He's really ambitious. I was in command before Jim. Look at him now. Up there and still going up. That's my secret, for what it's worth."

"It's a very interesting theory," said North quietly. He lit a fresh cigarette. "Have you ever discussed it with Jim?"

Stock laughed. "Of course. I'm always telling him he's a power hungry tycoon. He just laughs. We're very good friends. He doesn't scare me and, of course, I don't scare him. That's a good recipe for friendship. Lack of mutual fear."

Gene grinned. "I didn't bank on getting philosophy with my automation. But thanks. It's been a very interesting afternoon."

"My pleasure," Mike told him. "Look, it's getting on. We'd better drink up if you want to see George Moffat's engine room."

"Right. What's the toast? The *Emperor*?"

"Yes, coupled with absent friends."

"Now we're back to Jim."

"It's his ship."

"That's true. That's why I can't understand why he's not coming out for the launch."

"That's probably why."

"Could you unravel that for me, please."

"Because you can't understand it. That's why. He's not coming out because he knew you would worry about why he's not coming out."

"Phew. Believe me, Mike, your mind's devious enough to take you anywhere you want to go."

"Here's another thought then. Have you checked up on him? Is he still with Inoco?"

"Now you're becoming ridiculous." North raised his glass.

"Don't be too sure." Mike was enjoying himself. "He's the type. Challenge, he says. That's what he's interested in, challenge. He must've just about sewn this one up now. Maybe he's sitting up on the tenth floor in London considering offers."

"Let's drink then—to his turning them down." He smiled across at the captain. But Gene North was not amused. This was a new thought. Jim Bruce was his ideas man. He could not afford to lose him.

CHAPTER SIX

The hot water was wonderfully soothing. Sonia wiggled her toes and watched the ripples fanning out across the steaming surface. She was back in their suite in the hotel. The bath was pale blue, big, with silver dolphins camouflaging the taps. It was an expensive American bath. Though still in her first day in Japan, she had long given up hope of being allowed to find out about local baths, or food or anything. At that moment it did not matter. The heat of the water was restoring her. She was tired after her afternoon in the yard and on the ship. Especially her feet. Someone should have warned her that high heels and a ship's ladders and catwalks did not mix. That apart, she had enjoyed herself.

Sonia's knowledge of ships was limited. She had gone on a Caribbean cruise in her early twenties in an attempt to forget about a man problem she had at the time. That trip had worked out very well but not in the way she expected. She had thought that the gay whirl of cruise life would take her out of herself, introduce her to other men, make her less obsessive about her problem. In the event it succeeded because it opened her eyes on a world she had never even suspected. It was said that the shipping company changed the whole crew of that liner every trip so that the men could cope with the demands of the passengers. One officer told her he always kept his cabin door locked to save himself from multiple seduction. After a few days Sonia would have believed the most unlikely story. She was jerked out of her depression by her sense of humour and the remnants of her strict upbringing. Her humour she got from her Irish mother. Her strict upbringing from her Swedish father. She came from the Middle West; her father was a small farmer. She had grown up with old-fashioned ideas about a woman's place. When she came to New York after secretarial college these ideas were soon eroded. As a single girl, country bred, let loose in the big city she was excited by the parties and the dates. Life was suddenly thrilling. But she was not ready for the consequences. She had man trouble, she tried to cure it by not going out, she was lonely. She started going out again, she joined in, and she fell very hard for another man. He was married but claimed that was no problem. Sonia was not so sure; she kept remembering her father. Hence the cruise. Watching the other women, seemingly possessed by an infectious nymphomania before the ship was properly clear of the harbour, she thought about home and the wine her mother used to make. If the bottles were plugged too tightly when the fermentation started, the corks would blow out all over the kitchen like a volley from a badly trained firing squad. You could lose a lot of good wine that way. It was as simple as that. Sonia grew up overnight. She saw the funny side of human relationships. After that cruise, life was good. She took more interest in her work, she got on. She still went out a lot, she had a good time, but she was in control. Few men can handle a woman who knows when to laugh.

She hardly ever thought about marriage. It had no appeal for her. Until Gene. She had been his secretary for four years. They got on well together. They understood each other. There were never dates, or week-ends, nothing like that. Then it just happened. His second divorce was through. He asked her. She thought about it for a while then said "Yes." So far it had worked out very well. They lived quietly. He was pleased to be free of the society life his first two wives had lived. She knew about his work. They could talk. They were starting to fall in love.

She moved her body in the water and sighed. That's the trouble with hot baths. I wish Gene would come back. I'm a real sucker for older men. Like that commodore. He's sweet. Very British. Tall, a bit gaunt, well scrubbed, neat, and that mane of silver hair. Pity about his fingers. I wonder how they got scarred and twisted like that? He's a bit self conscious about them, always has his hands made up into fists. I wonder why he never married? Very gallant the way he explained it to me. A bit shy, sort of embarrassed. "I—I've just never been lucky enough to meet someone as attractive as you, Mrs. North." Sweet.

He was better after Gene went away with that funny staff captain. He seemed to relax with the big boss out of the way. Odd that. Gene's so easy to get on with. I suppose it's not Gene, it's just that some people don't ever meet people, they just meet ranks and positions. Maybe spending a life at sea does that, all these years of having to say "sir" all the time. You must get to feeling that some people are god. Or maybe being a sailor makes you uncomfortable with shore people. The commodore's like that. He was uncomfortable with Vic Grosset and that film crew. Even though he was on his ship, at home, and everyone else kept losing their way. She smiled. Oh and when that make-up girl started patting his face with a powder puff, I thought the old boy was going to explode. Wish I could have heard what he was thinking. Full marks again to Vic though. He's not my favourite type but he had that situation all worked out in advance. That's why he invited me. He didn't really need me in that film. He only needed someone to get the commodore relaxed and talking naturally. It seemed to work. They just followed us around with a camera. It should be a good bit of film. Of course the ship will steal the show. Gosh but that ship really is something. So big, long anyway. More than a quarter of a mile from one end to the other. Didn't seem very big up the way, not like that liner I was on. But then the commodore explained that; most of this ship is under-water. They don't need all these cabins and public rooms like a liner. It's very nice inside though, better than that liner. All the cabins big and air-conditioned and easy to clean; and the recreation rooms, and a library, and a little cinema. That gorgeous swimming pool too; I'll spend a lot of time in that. It's going to be a good trip, a real holiday. I wonder what the food will be like. The kitchen seemed awfully small. I must ask about that. The commodore certainly wasn't overweight. No, it must be all right. Just think about that staff captain. He seemed well fed. I must talk to him. He didn't look like a sailor at all, more like one of those jolly, plump monks you used to see in the movies. He even had a bald patch. I wonder how Gene got on with him? They were going to some shed or other to see all that fancy equipment. That was another surprising thing about the ship. There didn't seem to be any of these big wooden wheels and compasses. No funnel either. Every-where you went was packed with banks of dials and switches and levers. It all looked more like the computer centre in New York than a ship.

Oh, that was a lovely bath. Now I feel fine. She pulled her-self to her feet and stepped out. She wiped the mist from the mirror and studied her dripping reflection. Not at all bad, Sonia. Your figure's not suffering from the lazy life anyway. She wrapped herself in a huge towel and went through to the bedroom. Come on, Gene, come home. Quick, before I have to start dressing for this party.

It was almost six in the evening before Kim got away from Grosset. She had had a busy day. In the morning she had been down at the shipyard going over all the details for the launching ceremony and the trials that were to follow. She had also checked that the yard knew about the Norths' visit in the afternoon. She only saw Mike to wave to. After lunch she met the hotel manager to go over the arrangements for the party. It was not her responsibility at all—it was Inoco's party—but Grosset had asked her to stand in for him as he was going down to the ship with the Norths. She had agreed to do it. She knew what was wanted and she knew the hotel staff would work better for her than for anyone else. There was a fair amount of influence in being a protégée of Mr. Yashawa. She need not have stayed. Everything was perfectly organised. But she checked it all. She was almost wholly westernised but she was proud of her own people as she did her rounds. The lie that the Japanese could only copy was everywhere exposed. If it had ever been true, it was certainly a thing of the past now. Her people could improve on almost any idea from Europe or America. The new ship was proof of that.

She was leaving when Grosset arrived, full of apologies, explaining how Mr. and Mrs. North could not do without him, wanting to start checking the party details yet again. She told him everything was perfect, then he insisted on buying her a drink for all her trouble. It was as if he could not bear his own company for the couple of hours till the party began. She refused. She had a lot to do.

Back in Mike's room, she lit the charcoal in the *hibachi* and sat waiting for the kettle to boil. There was no sign of Mike. He'll be busy getting ready for the trials tomorrow. Oh, my head. She told herself she was just tired. The party will send it away. No, I'll get Mike to massage my neck. That always works. Suddenly she thought that the headache might be premenstrual. She tried not to think about that. Where's my diary? I'll check the date. No. It can't be. It mustn't be. We've got so little time left.

77

The kettle boiled and she made tea. She took some aspirin and drank two bowls of tea. She went over and slid along the door of the wardrobe. She thought for a bit about what dress to wear then she chose the *cheong-sam* in white shark-skin with gold appliqué work on the collar. Mike had been with her when it was made. She had protested that it was Chinese, not Japanese. He said he liked it. He liked the mandarin collar and the side-split skirt. It was simple. It suited her. She lifted it out on its hanger. Almost half past six. Where has he got to? She took out his uniform and brushed it. She smiled. He hated uniforms, particularly this one. His shape was better camouflaged in loose fitting civvies. She laid it down and went back and made some more tea.

She sat on the quilt, sipping from the bowl, trying to make her headache go away, trying not to think about Sonia North. It was crazy but ever since she had seen Sonia she had been trying to keep her out of her mind. She had expected Mrs. North to be of an age with her husband. But she was young and beautiful. That blonde hair brushed down over her shoulders, that sunbrowned skin, that bosom, those hips. And she was going to sail on the ship. All the way to California, for almost two weeks. With Mike.

Kim shook her head. I'm a fool. She's the boss's wife. She belongs to a millionaire. I'm crazy. I think that every woman will fling herself at Mike. Like me. No, nothing will happen. He's just going away for a month or two, then he'll be back. But where is he now? Down at the ship of course. That's where she is. She's been there all afternoon.

Slippers sounded in the corridor. Kim jumped up and ran to the door. It was Mike. She held tight to him as he came in. "Mike-san, where have you been? What have you been doing? It's late. There's the party." She clung to him and questioned him till he stopped and put his hands on her shoulders.

78

"Easy, love. Easy. What's got into you? There's plenty of time."

She pushed her face into his chest. "I'm sorry, Mike. I'm tired. I wondered where you were. I've got an awful headache."

"Is that what it is? Well, we know how to put that right, don't we. Over here, Kim. Sit down. Go on, sit down and brew me some tea. That's it. Now I'll send that headache away."

She squatted on the quilt and started making tea. He sat behind her, his hands on her neck, his short, thick fingers massaging her flesh.

"That's lovely, Mike-san."

"Don't talk. Just make the tea." He kept his fingers going, high up where he could feel the hardness of her skull. He wondered what it was all about. She usually kept herself very much in control. But he asked no questions, not till the tea was ready. Then he stopped the massage and they sat facing each other, sipping from the bowls. He waited till he was finished his tea. "Now tell me what that was all about."

Kim shrugged. "I'm sorry, Mike. It was nothing. It's all right now. I was just desperate to see you. My headache's gone."

"Of course it's gone. What I want to know is what brought it on."

"Oh you know, I've been busy. There was the party to see to and lots of other things. I just got over-tired, I guess."

Stock nodded. "That's reasonable, I suppose."

"Tell me about your afternoon," she asked.

"There's nothing to tell. I spent most of the time in the training shed introducing the big man from New York to automatic sailorising." He grinned. "It got better later on. I think I found his weak spot. I think I'll have fun in the next week or two, now I know how to get at him."

79

"What does all that mean?"

"Nothing really. I just enjoy needling important people. It makes them seem more human. Gives me a bit of their power."

"You enjoy having power over other people, don't you, Mike?"

"What have I done to deserve that? No, I don't enjoy power that way. At least only if the people are bigger than me. Not with the crew for instance. That's just my job. Someone's got to be in command."

"How about with me?"

He laughed. "Me, with power over you. It's the other way round. Or maybe it's mutual."

"Yes, maybe that's it." Kim lifted away the tea bowls. "And Mrs. North, was she impressed with the ship?"

"I'm sure I don't know. I hardly saw her." Stock stared at her until her eyes dropped. He grinned. "Kim, you're a nasty-minded, gorgeous little bitch." He reached over and turned her face round to look at him. "That's what it was all about, wasn't it. You thought I was down there on the ship trying to get a leg across the boss's wife. Didn't you?" He was laughing at her.

She hit him full in the face with a cushion.

He fell back on the quilt, hooting with laughter. "Oh, the captain's wife was Mabel, Whenever they were able, She and the Mate would . . ." The cushion stifled the rest of the ditty. Kim held it down with the weight of her body.

"You shut up, Mike Stock. It wasn't that at all. I told you, I was tired. I've had a hard day."

Stock struggled free and stretched her across the quilt, straddling her with his legs. "Fibber," he said. "You're a fibber."

"I'm nothing of the kind." She squirmed but could not free herself.

"You are so. And I love you for it." He bent down and kissed her.

She twisted her head away.

"Mind you, maybe you've got something," he went on impishly. "Yes, you have. She's jolly good looking. Lovely figure. Efficient looking hips. Promising mouth. Young too; keen maybe. Her man's getting on a bit. He's probably past it."

Kim pushed him off and scrambled to her feet. "You're a pig."

"Whatever you say." He was still grinning. "How's your headache?"

"It's gone. Now I'm angry."

"Good. I like you when you're angry." He stretched out a hand. "Sign a truce?"

She glared at him, then slowly smiled. She took his hand. "All right. It was my fault, Mike. Let's not fight."

"Done." He tried to pull her down on to the quilt.

"Not that kind of truce, Captain. We've got a party to go to."

"Hmm, so we have. Pity. I tell you what. I'll behave like a gentleman if you'll scrub my back in the bath."

"Is that not what you would call a contradiction in terms?"

"Not me, I'd call it bliss."

Kim threw a bath towel over his head.

CHAPTER SEVEN

The commodore stepped out of the lift and checked his watch against the foyer clock. It was five minutes to eight. He had judged it to a nicety. He was to be one of the receiving group. He did not relish the job but he accepted it as part of his duty. Lang was never comfortable with crowds of people, particularly the hand-picked upper crust people who would be at this party. He could not keep up with the stream of new names and new faces; and party small talk was quite beyond him. If he had anything to say, he said it; if he had nothing to say, he kept his mouth shut. Greeting a group of new people, he would shake hands, smile rather grimly, and nod his head. It got him by but it did not make him the most welcome guest or host.

Lang looked round the foyer. There was already quite a crowd, doffing coats and hats, chattering together, hailing new arrivals. It was a mixed bag of sizes, shapes, and nationalities. Many were from the Tokyo embassies. Some of the women wore national costume; others, European style evening dress; a few, cocktail dresses. One or two of the young things sported mini-skirts. The men were more of a pattern, with dinner suits and tuxedos sharing the honours. There were a couple of Japanese in tails, looking for all the world like escapees from a pre-war cartoon.

The commodore tugged down his short mess jacket and walked towards the main reception room. He felt conspicuous in his uniform but no one gave him so much as a glance. But Lang liked his uniform. It made him feel different, it gave him that solitariness he valued. He often thought it odd that it was Bruce who insisted on uniforms for everyone on the *Emperor*.

Uniform had always been a subject of controversy in merchant ships. It was a civilian service. The idea of uniform was a relic of the old days of company livery. Most seamen objected to it. It was accepted in passenger ships but elsewhere the officers wore it sloppily, with khaki shorts, no ties, pens stuck in breast pockets, braid hanging off their cuffs, frames torn out of caps. Ashore no merchant navy men would be seen dead in it. In companies like Inoco, with a strong American influence, the idea of fancy uniforms was frowned on. Denims, a windcheater and a baseball cap was the style. But no longer. And it was Bruce, the Americanised Scotsman, who was setting the new pattern. Uniforms for the whole crew; a working blue battle dress for on board, a No. 1 suit for special, epauletted khakis for the tropics, mess kit for entertaining. And Inoco paid for it all. Lang remembered congratulating Bruce on his good sense. The reply was harshly commercial.

"My dear Lang, the *Emperor* and the ships that follow are going to be like peepshows. They're new. Everyone's going to want to come on board and peer. These ships are going to be the best free advertising this company's ever had. The image has got to be right. The uniforms are part of the image. It's as simple as that."

Lang kept his own counsel after that. But he believed that people like Bruce could do the right thing for the wrong reasons. Like that unique fifth strip of gold braid showing Lang to be the first acknowledged commodore in the company's history. And even Bruce had had to admit he was wrong about sweeping away all the old ranks. Of course he excused himself on the grounds of convenience and still published crew lists with his factory type ranks in bold and the old equivalents in brackets underneath. But on board the Captain was still the Captain, not the General Manager; the Chief Officer was still the Chief Officer, not the Operations Manager; the Chief Engineer was still the Chief Engineer, not the Maintenance

Manager. John Lang was going to keep it that way as long as he was there.

Gene and Sonia North were waiting in the reception room with Grosset and a secretary from the British Embassy ready to prime them with identification of the guests.

"Come on in, John," called North. "I was just telling Victor here not to worry about you. He thought you were going to be late."

"I'm not, am I?" Lang checked his watch again.

"No, no, right on the dot. You stand there, on the other side of my wife."

"Hello, Commodore," said Sonia. "Here beside me. You don't seem any the worse for this afternoon."

Lang smiled briefly. "I would have been, Mrs. North, if you hadn't been there. I hardly noticed the cameras or the microphones."

That's good, thought Grosset. We couldn't use that voice of yours. We'll cut it and dub in a commentary. "Can we start now, sir?" he asked North.

"Fire ahead. The sooner, the better."

Lang cleared his throat. "How long will this go on?"

"The party?"

"No, this hand shaking business."

"Don't worry, John," North told him. "We're not meeting everyone. Just those who'd be hurt if we didn't stick to the rules."

"Good. That's not so bad." Lang had his own plans for that evening.

The doors were swung back and the crowd outside moved forward.

"You're like me, Commodore," whispered Sonia. "I want to get on to the drinks and the caviare."

"It's not that, Mrs. North. I'm—I'm not at my best with people."

84

"Nonsense. I think you're a doll." She squeezed his hand.

Lang flushed. There was no time to reply. The first hand was extended and the first face was smiling toothily and talking. The commodore grabbed, shook, tried to smile, and nodded his head. Immediately another hand, another face, another name. It went on, in fits and starts, for almost half an hour. Lang looked dazed by the end but it was just that he had found a way of coping. The hand shaking and head nodding had become a sort of reflex; he was seeing past the people, seeing the guests across the room and through the big double doors in the next room. He noticed several of his officers and men. They were all in uniform; they all seemed to be smartly turned out. Of course, "men" in this crew was a relative term. It was really a crew of officers and petty officers. The whole deck crew, apart from the officers, numbered three, one man for each bridge watch, and each man a long-service quarter-master. No tearaways, thank God. Lang had worried when he heard that the *Emperor* was taking a white crew, not following the usual Inoco practice of having Indian crew men and British officers. But this white crew would be all right. Every one of them hand picked; and anyway, who would want to stir up trouble when they had a contract to work only half the year but get full basic pay, and unheard of basic pay at that, for the six months they were at home. There could be trouble of course. That all-jobs clause in the contract was made for troublemakers. But that was why these men were handpicked; so that no one would jib at anything they were asked to do if extra hands were needed. Lang did not like the new manning arrangements; they were too new, too much of a break with tradition; but if these nine months in Japan were anything to judge by, they were going to work. The commodore had often wondered how Bruce had got the men and the unions to agree to such a revolution. He was certain of one thing though. If it did not work out, he would get the blame.

Sonia North was tugging at his arm. "Wake up, Commodore.
It's all over. No more hands to shake, no more 'how d'you do's'
to say."

"I'm—I'm sorry, Mrs. North. I hadn't realised."

"I thought not. But you did it all beautifully. And all the
time you were away somewhere else. What were you thinking
about?"

"Nothing really. The ship, the crew. It's a big day tomorrow,
you know."

"You're telling me, Commodore. I've never launched a ship
before. Tell you what. Gene's away with Vic to talk to some
ambassador or other. Let's you and me have a drink to bolster
our courage."

Lang smiled. He liked Sonia. She was refreshing. She was
the kind of woman he would have liked to have met a long
time ago. "All right, Mrs. North." He signalled a waiter and
they helped themselves to Martinis. The drinks were ice cold
and very dry. Inoco was sparing no expense.

"Oh, I needed that," announced Sonia after her first long
gulp. "Hmm, I feel better already. Let's go through and see
who's in the other room."

They walked through, Sonia with her arm tucked into his.
They stopped in the other room and looked round at the throng.
The party was warming up; there was chatter and laughter all
round them. Some women looked round and nodded and smiled
then whispered urgently. Several men stared in frank admira-
tion at Sonia. A waiter passed with a tray and Lang got two
fresh Martinis.

"Tell me who everyone is," said Sonia.

"I don't know a soul. Except my crew, of course, and some
of the shipyard people." He pointed out the ones he knew and
told her about them. "All very ordinary, you see."

"I don't know about that. They sound a lot more interesting
than a lot of the others here. Look at that great oaf over

86

there. With all these medals, he must jingle when he walks."

Lang laughed. "How about some food?"

"Good idea. I'm famished."

They went over to one of the long buffet tables. Sonia helped herself to caviare and canapés. She had acquired a third Martini. She was feeling good. She saw Gene in the doorway listening to a little man in a tuxedo who was talking as much with his hands as with his mouth. Her husband looked up and smiled and waved. Thank heavens, thought Sonia. That's not his "Sorry, but you must come and meet this man" signal. I'm free for a bit.

"Commodore, isn't that your staff captain over there. There, with that Chinese girl. Or is she Japanese?"

"Japanese. Haven't you met her, Mrs. North? That's Miss Odinoku. She works for Yashawa's. The shipyard. Charming girl. Clever too."

"Yes, yes. Of course I met her. She was here at lunch. I didn't recognise her. It must have been that dress. She is charming, isn't she."

"Yes. Pity she's so friendly with Stock."

"Why? Is there a no-frat rule here still? I thought the occupation was over long ago." They're friendly all right, decided Sonia. They've still got that bright-eyed, breathless look of people not long out of bed, together. So what? Maybe I've got it too.

"There's no rule," said Lang. "It's just that I don't like to see a girl like that getting mixed up with a man like Stock." He sounded suddenly tense, strained.

Sonia watched him. That's odd. I wouldn't have thought you'd have borne a grudge like that. She wanted to say "They're over twenty-one, good luck to them." Instead she said, "He doesn't look very dangerous to me, Commodore. Rather nice, really. Sort of cuddly. Doesn't look like a big he-man sailor at all."

87

"Don't misunderstand me, Mrs. North. He's very competent. Knows this new ship inside out."

"But you don't like him."

Lang looked uncomfortable. "As a man, no. He's married. In England." He shuffled his feet and drained his glass. "This is between us, Mrs. North. Don't say anything to your husband. Stock does a good job."

"Our secret," she promised and finished her drink.

But the bond was broken. Lang knew it and excused himself. He was sorry to leave her but glad to be free of social obligations. He had more important things to do than gulp cocktails and make pretty conversation.

Sonia smiled to him as he left. A waiter offered a tray and she took another glass. She watched Stock and Kim across the room. They seemed to be a little island in the moving, talking, laughing sea of people. Her three Martinis had made Sonia feel quite arch. I shouldn't but I'm going to. I'm going across there to talk to them. Anyway there's that thing Gene asked me to find out about. She started across the room.

Kim saw her coming. "Your boss's wife's on her way over, Mike."

He looked round. "So she is. Mrs. Millionaire herself. She was his secretary. Did you know that?"

"No. Is it important? How do you collect all that gossip about people?"

"I keep my ears open. It's a sort of game I play. I always like to have something unexpected up my sleeve."

"Maybe she's not coming here at all."

"Yes, she is. She's going to be very charming, then she's going to get round to asking me about Jim Bruce."

"That's the man in London, isn't it. Why?"

"Because I was naughty this afternoon and told her hubby something that worried him."

88

"That's your secret, isn't it, Mike. You always keep people on edge."

"Not always, darling. You're never on edge."

"I'm never off it with you. Watch out, here she comes."

Sonia sensed that they were talking about her. It did not bother her. What did bother her was that she felt overdressed in her full length ball gown compared to the simple oriental sheath the other woman was wearing. She pushed the thought out of her mind and smiled as she came up to them. "It's Captain Stock, isn't it? Hello."

"Hallo, Mrs. North," said Mike. "You've met Kim, haven't you."

"Hello, Kim. I think we were more formal at lunch. Kim doesn't sound like a Japanese name."

"It's short for Kimauko, Mrs. North."

"Call me Sonia, please. Kimauko—it has a lovely sound."

"It's really very ordinary if you're Japanese."

Sonia laughed. "I suppose that's true." She sipped her drink.

Stock felt that Kim was not at ease. He was sure that Sonia North had not come over just on impulse. "It looks like being quite a party before the night's out."

"Is that bad?" asked Sonia.

"Not if my crew's turned in by midnight. I don't want too many big heads tomorrow when we're running trials."

"But there's nothing for anyone to do in that ship. Everything's automatic, isn't it?"

"Not quite. We still need humans to press the buttons."

Sonia grinned. "I suppose you do." She took another sip. "Was that an oversight by the great Mr. Bruce?"

It was Stock's turn to grin. Smoothly done, Mrs. Millionaire. "I hadn't realised you knew Jim."

"I met him once or twice in New York."

"Don't you worry about Jim and his buttons. He's got all his on. Didn't he strike you that way, Mrs. North?"

89

"Well, he didn't actually strike me. But he seemed very capable."

They all laughed. Kim had to force it out. Suddenly she felt hemmed in by the crowd, hot, flushed, uncomfortable. She knew it was stupid but she wanted to be away from Sonia North. Away from Mike even, just for a while, till she felt better. "Will you excuse me?" she said. "I have to go up and tell Mr. Yashawa how the party's going."

"Why is he not here?" asked Sonia. "He should be the guest of honour. Bring him back with you, Kim."

"He wouldn't come. He doesn't like parties. He's not as young as he used to be."

"Who is?" put in Mike. "I've got a theory, Sonia. I don't think there is a Mr. Yashawa. I think Kim runs this whole business. She just tells everyone there's a Mr. Yashawa because she thinks that is what they want to believe."

"You're a fool, Mike," said Kim.

"I know, darling," He patted her on the bottom. "Don't be long."

"Bye," said Sonia.

Kim turned at the door. Mike was talking and gesturing. Sonia North was laughing. Don't worry, Mike. I won't be long.

Mike was explaining his other theory about the mysterious Mr. Yashawa. He had tried it on Kim once, as a joke. She was not amused. For Sonia he embellished his story. It was funny in a cruel sort of way.

"You like making up funny stories about people, don't you, Captain."

"Do I?"

"Come on now, admit it. Gene was telling me before we came down to this party that you'd been telling him some wonderfully funny story about Jim Bruce."

"What one was that? Jim makes legends like other men make mistakes."

"I forget now. No, wait. It was something about Bruce being offered a job with someone else. Was that it?"

"You're supposed to be telling me."

"Oh, come off it. You know what I mean."

Stock grinned. "That was just a passing thought, Sonia. It could be true, of course. With people like Bruce you never know what to expect. I'll tell you something, though. If I was Gene, and I had a fellow like Jim under me, I wouldn't be going off on a two week jaunt across the Pacific."

Sonia took a sip. "I guess I'm supposed to ask why. Why?"

"Ta. Because, if I was Gene, I might come back from my ocean voyage to find my chair occupied."

Sonia laughed. "I won't tell Gene that, you know."

"Why not? It would give his ulcers something to work on."

"No ulcers. But really because nothing, but nothing, Captain Stock, is going to cheat me out of this trip." She drained her glass defiantly.

"Good. I'm glad to hear it. I'd have missed your company." He looked straight at her. She's just a little drunk now. She must have been a great secretary. Quite a woman, good to talk to, but not really my type. Maybe just as well.

The party thundered all around them. It had been carefully planned. There were enough guests to keep both rooms crowded. There was enough drink to loosen tongues and keep them flapping. There was enough food to tempt the strictest diet disciple. In case the chatter and the laughter was not loud enough to stun the ears, there was a jazz band in one room and a beat group in the other. It was the kind of party people talked about for days.

"You like female company, I hear," said Sonia.

"You've been talking to the commodore."

"That's true but I'd have guessed anyway."

"It's an even bet. You either like women or you don't. If you don't, you're queer. There's nothing queer about me."

91

"Oh, I don't know. Some people might think so."

Stock grimaced and shook his head. "You have been talking to the commodore. What'd he tell you? That I'm a married man and I'm carrying on with Kim?"

"He didn't say all that."

"No, he wouldn't. But he'd make it plain enough. He's a direct descendant of Calvin, you know. Did he tell you that? Or did you guess?"

Sonia smiled and waved her empty glass in front of his face. He stretched out through the crowd and grabbed a drink from a tray. She took a sip. It was almost warm but she did not complain. "Tell me about your wife, Captain."

"Why? You're not really interested. Let's talk about politics, or religion, or sex or something."

Sonia shook her head.

"All right. Her name's Janice, she's thirty, five foot three, rectangular, 40–40–40, homey looking, brunette sort of, and she's got a high pitched laugh and two daughters. More?"

Sonia nodded.

"Let me think. We've been married twelve years. I'd just got my Master's ticket and she claimed she was in the family way. She wasn't but it was a genuine mistake. The girls are nine and seven now. They're gorgeous. They don't take after either of us. They have their own zoo. At the last count there was a poodle, a pregnant puss, two budgies, a hamster, a tortoise and a grass snake. And we all live happily ever after in a house on the hill with roses round the door."

"It sounds wonderful, Captain."

"It's fine if you're a sailor and get away from it fairly often. By the way, the name's Mike."

"All right, Mike. Now admit that's not true about wanting to get away a lot."

"I'll do nothing of the kind."

Sonia took a gulp from her glass. It was not only warm, the

92

proportions were all wrong. The party was really under way. "Well, I must admit I've never met anyone quite as frank as you, Mike, on a few minutes' acquaintance."

"Why not be frank? It's the best way in the end."

"What about other people being frank? What if someone told your wife about Kim?"

He shrugged. "That's not frankness. That's bitchiness. Anyway, Jan wouldn't believe it. It's been tried."

"And she didn't believe it?"

"That's right. She hefted that particular woman a beauty across the ear with a Queen Nefertiti handbag I'd bought her at Port Said. The magistrate let her off. Said she'd been grossly provoked."

Sonia hooted with laughter and spilled the rest of her drink.

Mike grabbed the glass from her hand. "I'll get you another."

"No, don't bother, Mike. That last one was awful, anyway. The barman must be a bit tight." She mopped the liquor off her bag with a tissue. "I see now that I can't believe a thing you say. You just make it up as you go along."

"Please yourself."

"No, Mike, be serious for a minute. That's all fine for funny talk at parties. But you don't roam around the world setting your cap at women all the time, do you?"

"Of course I don't. What tankerman can? We're hardly ever in port long enough to draw breath. And anyway, tanker ports are always away out in the wilderness."

"So you admit it's all talk."

"No. When I get the chance and it comes up my back, of course I do."

"Like here in Japan, with Kim."

"I suppose so."

"Is it fair to her?"

"Sonia, don't lecture me. You sound like old Lang. Kim's a grown woman. She knows what it's all about. I may be a

93

bit of a rake but I'm honest. She knows about Janice and the girls."

"That must be awful for her." Sonia was suddenly sober. It was like an echo from the past. "Let's talk about something else."

"Whatever you say. You are the boss's wife after all. How d'you find Japan?"

She gave him a wan smile. "That's my line, Captain. How do you find Japan?"

"It's easy enough. You just walk out the door and there it is."

"It sounds easy. I read up all about it before I started out on this trip. All I've seen is an airport, a shipyard and a hotel. It's all the same as the States except that the faces under the caps and the helmets are oriental. And some of them don't look all that oriental. I fly all the way here dreaming about having a Japanese bath and sleeping on the floor and I finish up steeping in an American bath and snoozing on a bed so soft I'm sure I've slipped a disc."

"You should have booked into one of the Japanese wings. I've been there for months. I'll never be comfortable in a proper bed again."

"Wait a minute. You mean this hotel has Japanese rooms?"

"Of course. It's a Japanese hotel."

"Darn it. If I'd only known. It's not worth trying to shift now."

"Not a hope anyway. They're full up. Tell you what, if you want to see what it looks like, I'll show you my room."

Sonia stared at him. "I'm beginning to believe in your reputation, Mike. You'd like to show me your etchings, I suppose."

"You've got me wrong. I'll tell you a secret." He beckoned and she leaned over close to him. "You're not my type, Mrs. North."

"That's an insulting remark," she said with a smile.

94

"Sorry, but it's true. I like talking to you. That's all."

"More and more insulting."

"Do you want to see one of the Japanese wings?"

"I want to, but how do we get away from here?"

"Ladies do powder their noses. I'll meet you in the foyer."
She thought for a moment. "O.K."

He watched her weaving her way through the crowd. I wonder where the hell Kim's got to. She said she wouldn't be long. Old Yashawa must have asked her to count up all his yen. He made for the door.

When Kim got back to the party she looked in vain for Mike. How do I find him in this crowd? She stopped one of the waiters and asked. No, he hadn't seen the captain. Damn, damn, damn Mr. Yashawa. Tonight of all nights he wants to sit and talk to me. About the shipyard and the steel works and all the other companies, about how old he's getting and how much of a comfort I am to him. But never about Mike. He knows about Mike and me, he's known from the beginning. But he never talks about him, he pretends he's not there. The old are like that. Tell yourself a thing's not there, and it will go away. It's true this time, about Mike. After tomorrow, he'll have gone away. For weeks, months, maybe for ever. Damn, damn, damn. Where are you, Mike-san? Oh, there you are. Over there by the other door. She waved.

Stock was with the Norths. Sonia was telling Gene about her visit to the Japanese wing. Mike saw Kim and waved back. He excused himself and hurried over.

"Where have you been, love?"

She took his arm. "I'm sorry, Mike. The old man wanted to talk. I couldn't get away. I was glad to see the commodore."

"What's he got to do with it?"

"I wouldn't be here if it wasn't for him. As soon as he arrived, Mr. Yashawa let me go."

"I don't get it, Kim. Did that old fool Lang just burst into

95

the penthouse? Did his curiosity about Mr. Yashawa suddenly overcome him?"

"No, it wasn't like that, Mike. He seemed to be expected. He must have been invited. I didn't pass on the message but he must have been. Mr. Yashawa seemed pleased to see him."

"Well, never mind. You're back, that's what's important. If these two old codgers are yarning the night away up there, they can't bother us. Want something to eat?"

"No. Let's cook something when we get back to our room."

"Good idea. I don't fancy that caterer's food."

"Mike, it's terribly crowded in here. Let's go out on the terrace."

"O.K."

They went out and found a seat under a tree by the fountain. It was suddenly quiet. The stars were bright in the clear sky and it was deliciously cool after the heat of the party rooms. Kim pulled him close to her.

"How did you get on with Mrs. North?"

"Fine. I told her she's not my type."

"Mike, you are a fool. She could be important to you."

"Nonsense. I keep telling you. I don't need influence. I'm not going anywhere. It's wonderful not to be part of the rat race."

"I suppose it is. It's not so good when you're ambitious for something you know you can't ever get."

He cupped her chin in his hand. "I thought we agreed not to talk about that."

She nodded. "That's right. What were you saying to Mrs. North, apart from telling her she wasn't your type?"

"Nothing much. She's got a thing about Japan. She's been here a day and she hasn't seen all the things in the guide books."

"Did you tell her it's far better than the guide books?"

"Of course. I did even better than that. I showed her a bit of real Japan."

96

"How did you do that bit of magic?"

"I showed her what a Japanese style bedroom's like."

Kim jumped to her feet. "You did what?"

"You heard."

"I hoped I hadn't." She was very angry.

"Kim, love, keep your shirt on. What are you imagining? D'you think I took her along to our room and threw a leg across her? And all in five minutes."

"Shut up."

"Well, is that what you think?"

She paced up and down. Then she turned on him. "No, that's not what I think. That's not what's important. You just said it, Mike. Our room. Our room, and you took her there."

Stock shook his head and ran his fingers through his hair. "Women."

"No. Not women. Just that one particular woman. That one particular woman who's going to go away on that ship with you."

"Aw, come off it, Kim. I was only trying to spread a little happiness. I've told you it was nothing. What d'you want me to say?"

She stopped in front of him. "You don't know, do you. After all these months, you don't know. Mike, that's our room. It's special. To me anyway. I know nothing happened. It's just that you let her see it, as if it was a side-show, just another tourist attraction."

"All right, all right. I shouldn't have done it. I'm sorry. Now will you calm down." He was not pleading. There was impatience in his voice.

Kim sensed it. He was like that. You could push him so far then, suddenly, something cracked and it was as if he got the scent of the sea and wanted to be rid of people and commitments. She sat down beside him. "I'm sorry, Mike-san. It's not a good time for me. I'm a bit on edge."

"That's all right, love. It was silly of me." He patted her hand. It was an absent-minded sort of gesture, as if he was thinking of something else. The ship. The sea. Escape.

"Mike, let's not go back to the party. Let's go back to our room."

He nodded.

They got up and walked arm in arm across the courtyard. They could get into their own wing that way without going back to the party. A long high note from a trumpet sounded from inside the hotel, then it cut off and was replaced with applause and a surge of talk and laughter. Stock looked down at Kim suddenly as if he had just realised she was there beside him. He smiled and she gripped his arm fiercely.

CHAPTER EIGHT

It was true that John Lang had been expected up in the penthouse. Kim had been right about that. But he had not been invited.

All day he had been thinking about it. From that first waking moment when he recalled his decision taken during the night and realised, in the bright morning light, the absurdity of his idea that Mr. Yashawa could have any connection with his past. Shaving, he told himself not to be a silly old fool, but seeing his mangled fingers reflected in the mirror made him wonder. Eating meals, walking through the yard, meeting the Norths, spending the afternoon with Sonia on board the ship, he kept realising how crazy his idea was, set against the real world. It was ridiculous. He would only make a fool of himself. If he did get up into the penthouse and Mr. Yashawa reported it, the company would waste no time in taking appropriate action. He knew how Inoco handled situations like that. No questions, no arguments, no verdicts. Straight on to the first plane. That would mean losing the *Emperor*. Then he wondered if maybe that was what he really wanted. He wondered if he feared the new ship so much that his mind was concocting a complicated plan of escape. He dismissed the idea. But it was not easily dismissed. John Lang had spent his life doubting his motives, always questioning what appeared to be the easy way. He had been brought up to distrust any course that did not tax him to the limit.

By the time evening came and he was dressed for the party he knew he was going through with it. He had to know, he had to settle this question in his mind before he sailed away from Japan. He told himself he would be able to handle it. There need not be an incident. It was reasonable that the commodore of the new ship should want to meet the man who built it.

When Sonia North left him at the party, he went over to the buffet tables and ate some food. Then he moved around the room, talking to his officers, talking to other guests who talked to him. He did not want to make his move too soon. He felt that if he judged it right he would not be missed. The noise of the party grew, the temperature rose. He felt hot and a little sick inside. He knew the feeling. It was always the same when a big decision had to be made and there was time to think. It was fear that he would make the wrong choice. He escaped to the foyer.

No one seemed to notice him. He knew where the private elevator was. There was no one about. It was a quiet corner screened off by troughs of shrubs. He watched the indicator light. It seemed to glow for an age. He almost turned away. Then the light went out and the doors slid open. He stood quite still, hoping the doors would close again. But they stayed open,

waiting for him. He walked in and looked for the control panel.
There was none. The doors closed and he knew from the heave
in his stomach that he was speeding up towards the penthouse.
There was no going back now. He could make an excuse when
he got there. "Terribly sorry. Made a mistake. Must have got
into the wrong lift. Terribly sorry." No. He remembered that
jolting ride in the truck to the barracks. Not like this. This
time there was no feeling of movement. Like this. There was
the same feeling that something terrible was going to happen.

The doors slid open. A Japanese in a starched white jacket
was bowing in the hallway. "Good evening, Commodore." He
pointed the way. "Please."

Lang stepped out and followed the man. He reacted auto-
matically, dazed by the ease of reaching the penthouse, by
being met and known. He was expected. He had not even
considered this possibility.

The servant stopped and raised his hand. "Wait, please."
He went through a door.

Lang stood quite still, watching.

The door opened and a young woman came out. "Good
evening, Commodore."

"G—good evening," he said. Then he realised who it was.
"Good evening, Miss Odinoku."

She was already past him and hurrying down the corridor.
He turned and watched her. She looked back once as she went
into the lift at the far end.

The servant was back. "Please."

Lang walked through the doorway and stopped inside. The
room was softly lit. The shadows were deep.

"I am so glad you came, Commodore Lang. I've been
expecting you." The voice was clear, un-English in an unde-
finable way, and there was the quaver of age in one or two of
the words.

Lang stood still, his eyes swivelling, trying to trace the speaker.

"Do come in, please."

The commodore saw him now. He was silhouetted against the light from one of the lanterns. He was in a wheelchair.

"Mr. Yashawa?"

"Of course."

"I'm—I'm sorry to burst in like this. I—I . . ."

"Don't apologise, my dear chap. Come and sit down. I hoped you would come." The chair moved a few feet. "Over here. This is a comfortable chair."

Lang walked over and slowly sat down. He was facing Yashawa. The light was behind the old man; his face was in shadow.

"You don't have much to say, Commodore. Have I stolen your thunder by expecting you?" Lang said nothing so the old man went on. "You might have guessed that an old recluse like me would be protected by all the wonders of electronics. But that was not why I expected you. That just told me you were coming. I've been expecting you for some time. When today came, your last day, I began to wonder if I had misjudged you. I began to wonder if my years were beginning to cloud my judgment. So I'm glad you came."

The commodore stared at the silhouette. He was no longer afraid. He was confused.

"Shall I tell you why I expected you?" Yashawa paused then went on. "I hope you are going to join in the conversation later, Commodore Lang. But I understand your surprise. I've been expecting you because you have shown interest in me. I've been expecting you because I have, in my turn, shown some interest in you. I have many resources at call, Commodore. I have time on my hands too. I've been expecting you because I think I know why you wanted to come up here and meet me. Correction. See me. Is that not so? And I am being very discourteous by quite literally keeping you in the dark. Will I tell you why you came up here, Commodore?"

Lang sat forward and gripped the arms of the chair.

"Would you like a drink, Commodore? No. A cigarette? No." A long pause. "You came up here, Commodore Lang, to find out if I am, or used to be, a Major Kuno."

Lang started up.

"Please, please. Relax. Sit down."

Lang sat back down slowly. "How could you know that?" he asked hoarsely. "Unless . . ."

"Unless I am or was the said major." The old man laughed quietly. "My dear chap, you do me less than justice. I may be an invalid, but I have a very long arm when it comes to finding things out."

"So you say. Answer me this then. Are you Major Kuno?"

"You are very direct, Commodore. That is not my way."

"It's my way," shouted Lang, grabbing the lamp from the table by his side and thrusting it at the figure in the wheel-chair. It was not a strong light but the suddenness of the movement startled Yashawa. He sat up straight, his hands on the wheels of his chair. The light was strong enough for Lang to see his mistake. The face was an old man's face, wrinkled, shrivelled up. The skull was high domed, hairless. The old man looked frail, shrunken. The commodore sank back in his chair. "I'm—I'm sorry, Mr. Yashawa. That was unforgivable of me. I apologise."

"Why? You wanted to see me. That's why you came here tonight. Now you've seen me. Do you recognise me?"

Lang shook his head. "No. No, of course not."

"You surprise me, Commodore. I expected you to be more difficult to convince. Twenty-three years is a long time. How old was the major then? Forty-eight maybe. That would make him over seventy. Surely I look over seventy. They say we orientals age more quickly than you."

"No. I would have known Kuno. Twenty years, fifty years, it would make no difference."

"You forget modern medicine, Commodore. Plastic surgery can work wonders."

Lang stared at the old man. "What are you getting at? Why don't you just ask me to leave? That's what I'll do." He stood up. "My apologies for intruding on you, Mr. Yashawa."

"Sit down, Commodore. I'll get you a drink." He wheeled the chair across the room to a table with a drinks tray on it. "Scotch, isn't it? The real thing, of course. Not our excellent Japanese imitation. And water. The same quantity. No ice." He poured as he spoke. He wheeled himself back and held out the glass. "You see, I know a lot about you already. Go on, Commodore, take it. Take it and I'll answer your questions."

Lang took the glass uncertainly and sat down.

Yashawa watched, his eyes lingering on the claw-like fingers circling the tumbler. "That's better. You wanted to know what I am getting at. The truth, Commodore. I have my reasons but they are not important just now. And I'm asking you not to leave because I think you can help me find that truth. Maybe I can help you find it too."

"What does that mean?"

"Let me try some truths on you, Commodore Lang. Truth number one; you were not arrested in July 1945 for sabotage. The record says you were but the record's wrong. You were arrested for an alleged association with a Japanese woman. Is that correct?"

"Go on." Lang's voice was hoarse, his lips dry. His drink was forgotten, untasted.

"That woman was killed by Kuno's men. Is that a truth too?"

The commodore nodded. His eyes were fixed on Yashawa. It was the first time in all these years anyone had spoken about it. It was the first time he knew that anyone else knew about it. How could anyone else know? The records were there. The woman was not mentioned. Yashawa could not possibly know. Unless . . . unless.

"No, Commodore. That is not a truth. That woman was not killed. She was not tortured or even interrogated. She was not arrested."

"It's a lie. She was. She was torn to bits by these fiends. And for nothing. Nothing, I tell you." Lang was shouting. "Nothing," he added in a whisper.

"She was not killed. She's probably still alive, somewhere." There was a long silence. "Are you sure?"

"That she wasn't killed, yes."

Lang sat erect in his chair, trying to take in this new fact. He never doubted it was a fact. He felt sure that Yashawa was telling the truth. At that moment he did not wonder how the old man knew what no one but Kuno could have known. Lang only remembered that for almost a quarter of a century he had carried with him a guilt that never existed. No, that was wrong. It did exist. It had no basis in fact but he felt it so it did exist. He tried to sort out the puzzle in his mind. The woman had not been killed, not even arrested, so Kuno had told him of her torture and death to make him feel guilty. Why? Just to twist another human being, to make him believe what was not true, to make him hate himself for something he had not done? But he had done something. If he had ignored that woman, never looked at her, never savoured the scraps of food she left for him, then nothing would have happened. There would have been no report for Kuno to see. There would have been no interrogation. No punishment pit. No mangled hands. Lang held out his hands and stared at them. They need not have been so ugly. The surgeons had said they could improve them. He would have none of it. They worked well enough. He had wanted to keep them that way.

"Do you want to talk about them?" asked Yashawa. "Your fingers."

104

"You seem to know far more than I do. Surely you know about them."

"Only what the records say. They were like that when you were found after the bombing. It was assumed you had been tortured. But that's not true, Commodore. Your hands were all right when you were put into that pit."

Lang nodded. "I was half crazy after all the questioning. I wanted to get out. I scratched and scraped at the walls till I passed out."

"I see," said the old man quietly.

"No, you don't see," roared the commodore. "You don't see at all. You know it all but you know nothing. I scratched and scraped because I thought that woman's body was in the pit beside me. I wanted to bury it. I wanted to hide my shame. I wanted to bury her and my memories of Kuno and everything. And all I did was create a little legend." He panted for breath. "They gave me a medal for it. This one up here on my chest. A medal." He said it like an oath.

"Who ever deserves a medal, Commodore?"

Lang said nothing.

"You must really hate Kuno."

"Yes, I hate him. I loathe the sound of his name. Now, I suppose I hate him even more. But what's it matter? If it wasn't him, it would be someone else. Hate's something you feel because it's already inside you trying to find a way out. I suppose it's really myself I hate."

"That's a shrewd thought. It's a pity more people don't understand that."

Lang grunted. He kept his eyes away from the old man. He saw his untouched drink and picked it up. The taste of the liquor refreshed him. He looked up at Yashawa. "Well, is that the truth you wanted? I don't know why. You seemed to know most of it before."

"No, that was not the truth I wanted. It fills a gap. Maybe it

105

does help towards the other truth. I don't know. It does however confirm much of what I thought I knew about you, Commodore."

"How can I matter to a man like you?"

"Everyone matters to a man like me. People are my only real talent. That's the talent that built this town, this hotel, your ship. Being what they call a tycoon, Commodore, is just knowing about people. You can buy engineers and architects, statisticians and scientists, welders and shipwrights. These are skills that can be taught. But my special skill, knowing what makes people what they are, what motivates them, knowing how to manipulate them to do your will like puppets on strings, knowing how to bend their minds, to change the way they think; that can't be taught. It can be learned, but only by a few who have the talent. Maybe that's why I tried to learn more about Major Kuno. He seemed to have that talent."

"How did you know about him at all?"

"Through you, Commodore. Oh, don't look so surprised. You came out here to take command of the finest ship my yard has ever made. Maybe the finest ship any yard has ever made. I wanted to know what kind of man you were. I had the time. I had this stroke last year just before you came here. I had to live up here in this chair. I had the resources of course. Few doors remain shut to my money and influence. I soon found out about your time in the prison camp. I found out about your arrest and your return to the camp. I read the official versions. I knew instinctively that something was wrong about it all. So I cast my net wider. In it I trapped Major Kuno's diary. The occupation forces never saw it. It was found after the bombing. It was suppressed. It gave the kind of picture of a Japanese officer my people did not want perpetuated. But, perversely, it was never destroyed. It had your story in it, his side of it. He was a very thorough man. Vain, of course, He liked to record everything. That's how I know about Kuno, Commodore."

"So you found out about him and about me. What then?"

"Then I heard you were asking questions about me. Persistent questions. So I arranged for you to get negative answers. I was sure you were the kind of man who would follow them up. Then tonight I was quite upset because you had not followed them up the way I thought you would, and your time was short. But then you did arrive and I was very happy to see you."

Lang drained his glass. "I don't know why. If you wanted to see me so much, why not just invite me up. I asked to see you more than once. I was always refused."

"An old man's foibles, Commodore. I felt you had to make the effort to find out the truth. If you made it, then I thought maybe you would help me find out that other truth."

"What other truth?"

Yashawa turned his chair and wheeled it over to the window looking down over the town and the docks to the sea. "The truth about who I am." He stared out across his town. "You know me, Commodore Lang? I'm old Yashawa. Scrap dealer become millionaire. This is my town, my hotel, everything in sight is mine. I'm old Yashawa who in twenty short years has built an empire. Officially I am seventy-five years old, but I was really born twenty-three years ago, August, 1945, in a hospital in Nagasaki. You know Nagasaki, Commodore? That's where the second atom bomb dropped, the one no one remembers. They took me from a demolished house. I was burned about the face and head, my skull was smashed. When I came to I couldn't tell them who I was. They told me. My papers were intact. My name was Yashawa. I had been a scrap metal merchant. I was born in February, 1893, in a poor district of Tokyo. They built up a very convincing life for me from my papers. There were bank papers too. I was quite well off."

"What are you trying to say, Mr. Yashawa? Are you trying

to say you're really Major Kuno? I don't believe it. All these papers. Aren't they proof?"

The old man wheeled his chair back. "Maybe they are. I can't say who I may be. I don't know. But I do know one or two unlikely facts. Fact one; I woke up in that hospital able to speak English better than most Japanese ever can. Fact two; I had only been in that house in Nagasaki for a week when that bomb fell. That bomb fell exactly ten days after Kuno's barracks were destroyed and he was presumed killed. His body was never found. Fact three; when I read the major's diary I found I could anticipate every next move. Fact four; he said in that diary that he had made plans for after the war. No details, I'm afraid. Does all that give you second thoughts, Commodore?"

"No." Lang shook his head emphatically. "It's all circumstantial. You've built it all up in your mind." He shook his head again and laughed. "As I've done all these years."

"Maybe." Yashawa took Lang's glass and wheeled over and refilled it. He brought it back to Lang's chair. "Will you do me a favour, Commodore?"

"If I can."

"Good. Then let's pretend that I really was the major. What would you do?"

"It's ridiculous. You're nothing like Kuno, physically or mentally."

"I wonder. Physically, I agree. My injuries at Nagasaki explain that adequately. But mentally, that's something different. It takes a lot of ruthlessness to get where I've got, Commodore. And even if I did wake up in that hospital with a new personality, would that change my responsibility for what I'd done in my previous life? That's an intriguing question, especially if you are a Buddhist."

"I'm not a Buddhist, Mr. Yashawa. I can't answer that for you."

108

"You promised to do me a favour. It's important to me. Now tell me what you would do."

Lang took a drink and thought for a bit. "I don't know. Nothing, I suppose. What could I do?"

"You disappoint me. You're really a very gentle man, Commodore. I wonder if that was what they meant originally by gentleman. Let me give you the alternatives you have. One, you could kill me now. That would not be difficult, though it might be difficult to explain. Two, you could go away and report me to the authorities. You could stir up quite a fuss. In your country there are still a lot of people who don't like the Japanese. Three, you could ask me for money for your silence. No, that would be out of character. Four, you could tell me you knew my secret but would wait a few days to see what I did about it. That might be your best choice, Commodore. That would be the quiet way, no chance of questions about medals and records; and for me the opportunity to do away with myself without any scandal that might touch my empire. Of course, that way I could call your bluff and do nothing. Even if I did take my own life, that would be poor revenge for all your years of guilt and hate. But then you're not really a vindictive man. You would only feel a new guilt."

"I'm going, Mr. Yashawa. This has gone far enough." The anger was back in his voice.

"Hear me out. You might as well do it with good grace. You can't leave this penthouse till I say so." He waited till Lang sat down again. "Thank you. So let's suppose I decided to take my own life. It would be no great sacrifice, you know. I suffer a lot of pain, and I don't bear it with the stoicism you in the West think is the birthright of all orientals. But how would I do it? Would I take the Japanese way? Would I take that dagger on the wall and disembowel myself slowly and deliberately? Or would I do it the Western way with a handful of these, pills on my desk? What do you think, Commodore?"

"I think I should go. I've got a ship to take to sea in the morning."

"Yes, of course, so you have. Can I say that I'm very glad it will be under your command?"

"Thank you." Lang walked across the room. He turned at the door. The old man was there beside him in his wheelchair. "Thank you too for telling me about that woman. It should give me some peace. I don't know if it will."

"I hope so, my dear chap. It's me who has to thank you. You've made my evening for me."

Lang held out his hand awkwardly. "Well, goodbye, Mr. Yashawa. I'm just sorry now we didn't meet and talk a long time ago."

The old man took the outstretched hand in both of his. "Maybe we did, Commodore."

CHAPTER NINE

It was an odd launching ceremony. It was odd because the ship was already afloat. Sonia had seen this the day before but had thought nothing of it. It was not until she was in the yard manager's office waiting to go out with the official party that she realised that this was not going to be the same as launchings she had seen on newsreels. The yard men explained.

Here at Shinoto they had been building ships in dry dock for a long time. But even if they had not, they would have had to start with this ship. Its length made a normal launching impossible. There was just over a quarter of a mile from the end of the building dock to the sea wall. If the ship was slip-

launched, it would have had to be brought up in its own length.
That was impossible. As it was, it would be a tricky job for the
flotilla of tugs to ease her out of the dock, nudge her round with
only feet to spare, back her down to the main basin and turn
her again to head out through the breakwaters to the sea.
Yes, of course, they had had to build the dock specially for
this ship. There had been a dock there before but much smaller.
They had cleared land behind the old dock and built this new
one. The expense was worthwhile. There was no other dock
in the world big enough to take a ship of this size for its annual
dry-docking. Yashawa was certain to get all the Emperor class
repair work for several years at least. Another dock was already
being scooped out alongside this one. The future was big ships.
But no, of course the docks were not only of use for big ships.
This dock, and the new one, were both capable of being split
to take two smaller ships. Yes, it all called for careful planning.
But careful planning was one reason why Japan led the world
in ship-building.

Sonia was impressed by all this expertise but a little disap-
pointed. She had been looking forward to seeing the ship slip
away as if impelled by the force of her bottle of champagne,
then hear the grinding roar of the crutches on the greased
slipway, and be deafened by the thunder of hundreds of tons of
drag chains leaping and clanking and straining to slow the
monster's flight, then through the swirling clouds of rust and
dirt see the water rushing away in great waves to escape the
alien presence and the tugs bucking and rolling then fussing in
to pick up lines and take the strain and stop the huge ship
dead in the water. And the crowds would cheer and wave flags
and all the ships and factories would hoot and toot. That might
happen even now but Sonia could not imagine it would have
the same spontaneity or intensity as in a proper launching. No,
this was going to be an anti-climax. But then everything about
this trip had been that up till now.

It was almost time. The party trooped down the stairs and out and along the strip of red carpet to the steps up to the platform built at the end of the dock close under the ship's flaring bows. It was a fine day, with a bright sun and a cool breeze sweeping in from the sea, fluttering flags and swirling skirts. There was a huge crowd packing both sides of the dock. The shipyard workers were there in strength, given time off to see their ship named; their wives and relations were there; all the schoolchildren of Shinoto were there, the girls in blue gym tunics and white blouses, the boys in the traditional high collared, brass buttoned blue uniforms. They all had the morning off school to see the launching of the biggest ship in the world, built by their parents in sight of their schools. There were guests in various degrees of importance. The most favoured up on the platform, the less important in enclosures on either side. The world's Press was there in force and every crane and gantry held a full complement of photographers and camera men.

The yard manager spoke first. He spoke in English, pausing after each sentence for the loudspeakers to boom out the Japanese translation. He had nothing new to say. The usual stuff about pride in workmanship, the family spirit in the Yashawa companies, and in this case a special pride in having built something bigger and better than any other yard anywhere in the world. It was aimed at the workers and the Press. It was competent if not exciting. The cheers came at the right times and in the right proportions. Then it was Gene North's turn. He too had nothing very special to say but he said it with immense gusto. He spoke this way because, though he had to say what was expected of him, he had a great sense of occasion. Up there on that platform, he really felt the size of the ship and the scale of the project that bore its name. Gene was that kind of man. In the past he had pulled a lot of strings to get seats at the Trooping of the Colour in Horse Guards' Parade.

He had never been put off by the rain, the damp cushions, the interminable marching and wheeling, or the blaring music. He sat it out with the same joyful stoicism as the other well-bred people round about him. He knew what was proper and he got immense satisfaction from it. But like his neighbours he also had the wit not to over-rate an occasion. All the best occasions were revealing of their organisers and spectators. Particularly their organisers. Like this one, this launching that was not a launching. It spoke volumes about Jim Bruce.

Of course it was an accident that it was an odd launching ceremony. The size of the ship and the conditions at the yard had dictated that but it still had the Bruce stamp. Then the name of the ship, *Emperor*. There had been many suggestions but Jim had stuck to his first idea. Standing there, mouthing his prepared speech, Gene was certain that Bruce had wanted that title shouted and emblazoned in the country where it once meant everything and now meant no more than king or queen elsewhere. Then there was the business of dedication. Jim would have none of it. It was an irrelevance, he said. If ships were built well and run well, they didn't need God-speed. No, not even if someone could persuade a bishop to do the wishing. Anyway, ships were sailors' things and sailors distrusted parsons near their vessels. And finally, is it not insulting to perform a Christian dedication when you have had to get the ship built in a non-Christian country? In Gene North's mind there was also the lingering thought that Jim Bruce might just now not be there beside him because he was going about his own business in distant great waters.

Sonia stepped up to the microphones. "I name this ship *Inoco Emperor*." It was the shortest speech but it got most applause. She pulled the lever in front of her. I might've known. I don't even get to swing the bottle. The magnum of champagne swung away in the carefully calculated arc and at just the right velocity that a dozen experiments had proved correct. It shattered against the hull and the red and white bunting fell away to reveal the ship's name on each bow and the Inoco crest on the stem like a puny figure-head. The platform party clapped politely, the school children cheered obediently, the workers yelled and banged with hammers and spanners, and all the ships in the harbour sounded their sirens. Above all the noise, the *Emperor*'s own siren boomed its deafening salute. The platform party hurried down the steps and along the side of the dock to be put aboard.

Up on the bridge, at the control console, Mike Stock had watched the ceremony on the closed circuit TV mounted up in the bow to give the bridge a view of docking and anchoring. On the stern set he could see the tugs closing in to take their lines. He was glad it was all happening at last. Now, on trials, he would be able to see if all the work he had put in training the crew had been worthwhile. It had to be. He knew it would be. The ship was nothing without these men. But still he wanted to see it all happening out there in the sea, not on film, or on a computer controlled test circuit, nor even on the dock trials they had been running for the last couple of weeks. Just out there where it was always different. But not yet. The tugs would take the *Emperor* out of the dock and back her down to the turning basin, cant her round, then tow her out clear of the harbour. It had been agreed only to use the engines in the harbour in an emergency. If there was no emergency, it was better to wait till the open sea to try her out.

The commodore was excited. He had waited a long time for this day. He had fought for his right to be there. He had often wondered if he should have fought, if it might not have been better to take the easy way and let the new ship go to Stock. Now, standing there on the bridge, looking out along the furlong of deck to the bow, he was sure he had been right. This was to be his niche in immortality. The first man to command the world's biggest ship. Let's get on with it. Let's get loose from the land and away out there to sea. Let's get away from people. Let's get these trials over and done with and send that Jap pilot off my bridge. He's reminiscent, with his flat immobile face under that peaked cap with the high soft top. Yesterday, seeing him would have upset me. I would have seen him as Kuno and had my waking nightmare, gone hot and cold, sweating and shivering. Now I just want him off my bridge. That's something Mr. Yashawa's done for me. He seems to have laid my ghosts. Can't think why unless just because he talked about them and made me think differently about them. Whatever it was, I slept last night as I haven't slept for long enough.

"Guests are aboard, sir." It was the officer on the intercom. "Tugs fast aft."

Lang nodded to the pilot. The Japanese went out to the starboard wing of the bridge and thumbed the siren button. The main siren down aft boomed twice to signal the tugs. He pressed the other button and the electric siren above the bridge squawked its instruction to the riggers tending the bow lines on the deck. Even without the throb of its own power, Lang sensed the *Emperor*'s movement in the water. At the console, Stock watched the TV monitors. The gap of water between the bow and the end of the dock was lengthening. The strain was on the tugs' lines aft and the water there was thrashed white from the little ships' propellers. The intercom reported each movement of the bow moorings down the dockside. Each report was followed by the sound of the winches taking up the slack then straining to pull the ship farther astern. The two sirens boomed and squawked, tugs hooted in reply, whistles shrilled, men ran, lifted, pulled, laid and waited. The intercom spoke calmly, painting a picture for the men on the bridge. The bow was half-way down the dock and already, looking aft, it was as if the stern was within inches of the sea wall. It was only a frightening illusion. The monitor screens proved there was still plenty of room. But that gap was closing fast. A flurry of hooting and booming and squawking. The six stern tugs divided, three on each quarter, and came ahead to halt the giant's progress. The men on the winches held on to the ropes, easing them in slowly now just to pick up the slack, heaving not at all. The *Emperor* slowed then stopped. Her stern almost overhung the sea wall, her bow was snugged in tight at the dock entrance. This was the crucial bit of the whole operation. Now, with only a few feet to spare at either end, the ship had to be swung round broadside to the dock and the cheering crowds. The crowds sensed the crisis and fell quiet. There were four tugs crowded under the starboard bow, three taking lines from that side, one taking one round the stem from port. Two tugs nestled under the port bow holding the ship off the corner knuckle of the dock. The breeze was light but not to be ignored with the vast target of the *Emperor*'s sides exposed in minimum ballast.

The tugs were ready. The pilot signalled. The tugs on the port quarter pulled. The tugs on the starboard bow pulled. The tugs on the starboard quarter waited with slack lines to check a too strong swing. Under the port bow the two tugs pushed at full power with their fendered prows against the hull. For a few seconds there was no movement. It was as if the *Emperor* was loath to leave her birthplace. But there was nothing now tying her to the land and suddenly she swung away as if realising her freedom. Sirens, hooters. The tugs changed positions like well marshalled troops on a parade ground. She was round, broadside on, and dwarfing everything in sight. Her size kept the crowds quiet for a few moments. Then, as she started moving astern across the harbour, there was renewed cheering. The tugs stopped her again in the turning basin then slowly swung her round to point between the breakwaters. Change of positions again. Three tugs fine on either bow, the rest close astern, fanned out on each quarter.

Sirens and hooters. The bow tugs' lines came tight, their screws thrashed the water at full power. It seemed an age before the *Emperor* moved. Slowly, then more quickly, the huge ship moved ahead. Her bows were between the breakwaters. Through. The stern tugs crowded close together. Bridgeworks through. After deck through. Poop through. Tugs through and clear. A long blast on the siren. Four of the stern tugs dropped clear. A long scream from the midships siren and four of the bow tugs cut loose.

The pilot came in from the wing of the bridge. "This heading will take her clear, Commodore."

Lang nodded. "Thank you. Steady as she goes, Quartermaster."

"As she goes, sir." The quartermaster was in his high chair at the after end of the lower part of the bridge. His hands rested on the two rudder levers. No wheel on this ship.

Lang looked up at Stock behind the console. "Dead Slow Ahead, Captain."

"Dead Slow, sir."

There was no need for extra instructions. Everything had been worked out weeks before. The Chief Engineer would slowly bring the engines to Dead Slow, check carefully, then tell the bridge he was ready to increase speed. The tugs would run on with the ship till Lang ordered them away.

They all felt that first gentle throbbing of the engines. Soon there was the sigh of the ship's own wind as she gathered way and the splash and gurgle of displaced water.

"Steering?"

"Like a dream, sir."

They all waited for the intercom. "Bridge. Ready to take her up."

"Thanks, Chief." Stock watched the commodore. He nodded. "Slow Ahead, Chief."

"Slow Ahead it is."

Immediately the throb of the engines increased. The ship was still in minimum ballast and needed more water in the tanks to sink her to her running draught. "Ballast now, sir?" asked Stock.

Lang nodded.

Stock flicked a switch on the console. "Operations Room. Programme One ballast."

"Programme One, sir."

Stock lay back in his chair. From now on it would just be routine.

"I don't need the tugs now, Pilot," said Lang.

The sirens sounded and the tugs sheered off. The intercom reported all clear fore and aft. Now the mooring parties could disperse to their proper stations. The whole crew was in for a hectic eight hours. The *Emperor* was on trial.

The guests were also in for a hectic eight hours. Different though. They were not allowed into any of the working spaces. The only sight they got of the bridge, or the operations room, or the engine control room, or the actual engine room, was on a quick conducted tour while the ship was working up to speed. Even then they had to queue up and peer through windows and portholes. The main decks were free to them for half an hour after that but access was then forbidden as the ballast and pipeline testing got under way and the decks swilled with gushing water. But the rapid tour and the short time on the open decks had been nicely judged. Well nurtured skins and careful hairdressing were by then starting to suffer from exposure. The right place then to be was in one of the recreation rooms or the big messroom aft where the caterers had ready a vast assortment of food and drink. For the young things with hands to hold or eyes to gaze into, the swimming pool area on the poop was decked over and protected from the ship's wind by its thwartships fashion plate. From midships to aft, the raised catwalk offered a safe route for any guests wanting a change of scene.

The Norths had their own rooms on the lower bridge. There was a bedroom and a sitting-room, both big, and a bathroom. But that day Sonia and Gene had guests to look after. They went from room to room, meeting and talking to faces already forgotten from the party the night before. Gene enjoyed it. He had the ship to talk about and all the other developments that made up the whole Emperor project. Sonia put up with it cheerfully. It was no worse than a too long cocktail party ashore but with the encouraging thought of a long, quiet, unsocial sea voyage to follow. Everyone ate and drank and talked, became cheerful or morose, ate, drank, talked, laughed and giggled some more and saw nothing of the strenuous programme of test and re-test going on in the forbidden spaces all over the ship.

It was a bad time for Kim. She now knew that her headache the evening before had been pre-menstrual. The first day was always hell for her. She was not the type to give in to it. She always took especial care with her make-up and her clothes. She had tried all the pills. None of them did much good. Being normally civil took extra effort. She could have done without the launching and this shipboard party. But she coped surprisingly well. Now and then she escaped for a few minutes to the open deck round the lower bridge and let the wind pluck at her hair as she stared away to the horizon or gazed down into the water rushing white and effervescent along the ship's side. She tried not to think about Mike but that was asking too much of herself. It was a cruel twist of fate that this was to be their last night together. Why did it not happen one day later, just this time?

Twice, she slipped up the outside ladder to the bridge. She just wanted to see Mike. She saw him through the huge circle of window that opened the whole horizon to the officer at the bridge console. She saw him but he did not see her. She wanted to speak to him, to hear his voice, to feel his hand on her aching body. She envied the photographers who were there inside the bridge. She was tempted to break the rules and ask to go inside. She would have been let in. But she just looked and went away. She knew her man too well. This was his world; she belonged ashore. If she had gone in, he would have looked surprised, then pleased, then said "Hallo," and chatted to her, and shown off some of the equipment. And only Kim would have been able to sense his disappointment that she had invaded a part of his life where she had no place. No, I can wait. It's only a few hours. I'll go and have a drink and something to eat; and talk to some of the guests and try and avoid being left alone with that awful man Grosset; and tell myself not to think what I always think when I see Sonia North. Not too long, just a few hours. Then I'll have Mike to myself, in our room, in our world. It won't be perfect, can't be, not tonight, but it will be us.

Stock was enjoying the trials. True they were routine in that the whole programme had been worked out in advance and rehearsed a dozen times. True that most of the tests had been done before in the dock trials. But this was different. The *Emperor* was at sea and really alive for the first time. And she was thriving. Test followed test and the pile of report sheets grew. They spelled out the quality and reliability of the ship and her equipment. Every piece of equipment was run at an overload of at least fifty per cent. It all held up magnificently. Specialists were there on the spot checking, tightening, tuning all the time. It was routine but it was the kind of routine Stock liked. Successful routine. Trouble-free routine. All the bridge equipment was 100 A1. All the operations room tests reported the same results. The midship joint was reacting well to the changing ballast programme. Pipelines, pumps, tank washing,

communications. All 100 A1. It was the same in the engine
room. In three hours they had the huge ship up to full power
on both propellers and, with only medium ballast in the tanks,
she almost reached 18 knots. Her first crash stop brought her
up in a mile and a half. The Chief thought they could cut
half a mile off that with a bit of practice. The distance would
be farther fully loaded but it was good for a ship of her size.
After that, they switched the engines to direct control from the
bridge. Stock revelled in that. He kept the intercom open to
the engine control room and gave the Chief a running commentary.

"It's as easy as falling off a log, George. Where's all that
engineering know-how you're supposed to need? Up to Half
Ahead. D'you see that? Simple. I just push a lever. It's
easy, I tell you. Watch now. Up to Full. There. Child's
play."

George Moffat took it all in good part. It had taken more
than a hundred years, but on the *Emperor* oil and water had at
last been blended successfully.

For Commodore Lang it was enough at first just to be there
on the bridge of his ship at sea. There was little for him to do
except listen to the reports coming in of successful tests. He
stayed out of the wheelhouse and control room most of the
time. Being at sea was for Lang a physical experience to be
savoured. It was best out in the wings of the bridge. There,
he could feel the ship through his feet on the deck and his
hands on the rail, he could smell the sea and feel the wind on
his cheek, he could hear the water and see the sky. He knew it
would take time to get accustomed to the *Emperor*'s size. From
the bridge, it was a big ship's length for'ard to the bow. And
another big ship's length and more aft to the stern. From port
to starboard she was as wide as two super-tankers lashed
together. Lang knew he would soon come to terms with its size

and power. He would even come to accept all the automation, and that new fangled midship joint, maybe even the new manning schedules with their blurring and eventual extinction of age-old ranks and responsibilities. But as the first excitement of having his new ship under him at sea faded, he started to notice things he would never come to terms with. They were temporary but none the less exasperating for that.

There were the photographers. In the bridge, down on the decks, in and out of the cabins, everywhere making the crew pose at their jobs like so many male models in these husky, highly coloured ads in the glossy magazines. Up in the sky in these two aeroplanes. The helicopter trailing the ship round every twist and turn, filming the wake and the bow wave for analysis ashore. The light plane zooming about searching out crazy angles to snap the ship from and maybe collect a photo-of-the-year award. There were the guests, there to ooh and ah, but really to eat and drink and gossip. Shorewallahs. Lang went down twice to mingle with them but soon excused himself back to the bridge. There was the harbour pilot, standing on the bridgefront hour after hour, still and expressionless. There was that Jap flag billowing at the stern. Every time he looked aft to thrill and wonder at that widest ever wake to be traced across the sea, that flag caught his eye. He was glad when they closed the land again and started manoeuvring trials. He went into the wheelhouse then. There he could give orders and watch and feel his ship and crew obey. The *Emperor* handled superbly. He took her in slowly to the anchorage off Shinoto. The sun was gone and the twilight was deepening. The lights of the town and the harbour were on. It was almost eight in the evening when the *Emperor*'s anchor cable roared out of the hawsepipe for the first time.

The tender was alongside at once and the guests were soon on their way ashore waving and shouting happily. One ceremony still had to be performed. The Norths and the yard manager came to Lang's day cabin. The papers were ready. Gene North signed. The yard manager signed. Then Lang signed. At last the *Emperor* was really his. Tomorrow, at first light, the Red Ensign would fly at the stern.

CHAPTER TEN

It was another half-hour before Stock came down from the bridge. He had stayed away on purpose. He had little time for ceremonies. The shipyard officials had gone ashore, the Norths had gone to their own quarters. The commodore was alone in his day cabin. He had served drinks to celebrate the signing over of the ship. That first drink had started to loosen the tension of the long day. He was sitting down, cradling a generous second whisky, when his staff captain arrived.

"Hallo there," said Stock. He walked in without waiting for an invitation. and plumped down in an arm-chair. "You're all alone. Is all the official drivel over then?"

Lang put down his glass. He was determined to be good humoured. "Yes. Everyone's gone. It's all signed for. It's really ours, now."

"You mean it's all yours, Commodore. How does it feel to be skipper of this great hulking barge?"

"Good, I suppose. Very good. It'll be better tomorrow, at sea and with our own flag up."

Stock grinned. "That's important to you, isn't it. Flying the right flag, I mean."

"Of course it is. Isn't it to you?"

"No, what difference does it make? I've sailed Panamanian in the old ships. It was just the same. Except that I liked having that ticket all done out in Spanish certifying me as a Capitano." He chuckled.

"I suppose it's a sign of my age that I don't like having to pretend to be something I'm not. I'm not ashamed of being British."

"Nor am I. But why be proud of it?"

"I'm not sure you'd understand, Captain. It has to do with tradition and history."

"Is that so? Tell me, is it one of your traditions not to offer your staff captain a drink?"

Lang was annoyed with himself. Stock had the knack of putting him out of step. "I'm terribly sorry." He got up and went over to the drinks locker. "What's it to be?"

"Scotch will be fine, thanks."

The commodore poured the drink and took it over to Stock. "Help yourself to water."

Mike doubled the drink in the glass and held it up. "Well, here's to you, Commodore. And your ship. And your flag."

Lang took a deep breath. "I'll drink to all these things, Captain, and I'll ignore your flippancy."

"Quite right too." Stock took a sip. "Hmm, that's better. I don't often feel I need a drink but I must admit I really needed this. That was quite a long day we had to ourselves."

Lang was relieved that the rough edge had gone from the conversation. He sat down. "Can I propose a toast?"

"Why not?"

"I'd like to propose a toast to you, Captain Stock."

"That's a turn up for the books. Why?"

"Because you deserve it. You've worked very hard training the crew, getting all this new-fangled equipment installed. And for today. I've run trials on new ships more times than I care to remember. It's never gone as smoothly before."

"That's very civil of you, Commodore. I'll drink to all that." He drained his glass. "Tell you what, I'll have another drink

since you're in a generous mood." Pompous old crow, thought
Stock. Handing out compliments as if he was God or something. Suppose that's how he sees himself. The great big shipmaster. Lord of all he surveys. He's living so far in the past,
he belongs in these history books he's so fond of. Ah, well, let
him have his head. Jolly him along. That was my brief from
Jim Bruce. Not so brief. I've been lumbered with him for
almost a year now. Why can't he be his age? Why can't he
just bow out quietly, retire and go and live in Bournemouth
and take his constitutional along the front and feel proud when
the old ladies say "Good morning, Commodore," and then
confide in each other excitedly what a fine figure of a man he
still is and not married either. Watch it, Mike boy. That
must've been a powerful drink. Remember you don't drink
much. And you've had nothing to eat since lunchtime. What
the hell. He took the refilled glass from Lang and splashed in
some water from the jug.

"Well, Commodore, what'll we drink to this time?"

"Anything you like, Captain." That's typical, Lang told
himself. No control. No real stamina. Tiddly on just one drink.
He may be a shipmaster but not in my book. No dignity.
That's it. No sense of occasion.

Stock was holding up his glass, his eyes half shut in thought.
"Got it. Let's drink to the girl on the hill."

"What girl on what hill?"

"You don't know the girl on the hill? You should, Commodore. She's ideal for you."

"I'm sure it's a joke but I'm afraid I don't follow it."

"No use following that one." Stock laughed. "The girl on the
hill. She won't but her sister will. Here's to her sister." He took
a drink then stared across the table at Lang. "Not funny, is it,
Commodore? You don't think so anyway."

"Not especially." Lang sipped his drink and laid it down.
He was annoyed but very sure of himself. He was not going to

be goaded into some sort of scene. He was going to make allowances for Stock. The man had had a long day and had done very well. They had to sail together. They had to learn to live together. It was different now. They were on a ship. It was not like being ashore. There it was easy to be apart most of the time. Here on board that was impossible.

Mike was enjoying himself. He was certainly not drunk but he was relaxed and that was as good as with him. "Not especially," he repeated. "That was predictable. Funny thing about you, Commodore. I don't believe you've ever had a good belly laugh at a dirty joke in your whole life."

"I wouldn't deny that. I've never found smut amusing."

"Pity. It is, you know. Not always, of course. But often."

"Why don't we agree to differ about that, Captain. I don't think we should quarrel about it."

"I'm not quarrelling." He took a drink. "I'm just saying that you're missing a lot of fun. And that's a great shame. So many times I can think of funny things happening and you didn't think they were funny. It was more like the end of the world to you."

"So you say, Captain. Maybe we should break this up now."

"No, no. Let's stay a while. I like talking to you. You stimulate me. Now I've just thought of a very funny case in point."

"You don't say."

"Yes, I do say. Very funny. D'you remember when that quartermaster got himself a roaring dose of Jap clap?"

"I do. And I'm damned if I see anything funny in that."

"True. Not funny. Very nasty indeed. But they fixed him up in no time at all at the hospital. No, Commodore, what was funny was what you said when I told you." Stock paused. "D'you remember what you said? No, I don't suppose you do. Well, you said, 'If I had my way I'd stick all their pricks in a bucket of caustic.' Remember? And I said that I hoped you meant to include me out of that little lot. And the funny bit was that you didn't think you'd said anything funny."

Lang breathed hard. "I hate to disappoint you, Captain, but I still don't."

"Good for you. I like a man who sticks to his guns." Stock drained his glass. "But you're all mixed up, Commodore. You've got morals and sex all mixed up. You're not alone. There's a lot of people who think like you do. They're all wrong. Now, take me for instance. I think I'm a very moral person. You don't agree, do you?" He waited in vain for an answer from Lang. "No, I know you don't agree. You think I'm an absolute rotter because I like company in bed. But I'm moral because I'm honest. Think about that, Commodore. I'm honest. I don't mean I'm outspoken though I'm certainly that. No, I mean I don't steal. I don't take anything that doesn't belong to me. Now you'd say I'm condemned out of my own mouth. You'd say that because you think I steal other men's wives or other men's daughters. But you'd be wrong. You can't steal a wife or a daughter because they don't belong to anyone. At least they only belong to themselves. Their bodies are their own and they're entitled to do what they like with them. It's just about the only really personal gift any human being can hand out. And if the law says different, then the law's an ass. No, when I mean stealing, I mean taking property, money, that kind of thing." Mike picked up his glass. It was empty so he put it back on the table. "I'll tell you something, Commodore. When I was a kid, I stole a quid out of my mother's bag. She found out. She didn't belt me or anything. She just looked at me. Then she talked to me, quiet like. She made me feel a right heel. Maybe that was what did it. Anyway I've never stolen since. I've got the same kind of thing about stealing as you've got about sex. No, don't say it, Commodore. You're going to say you're honest too. Don't. Just think about all the perks you got from ship chandlers before Jim Bruce brought in his purchasing department. Oh yes, sure, it was part of the pay, everyone knew about it. But did you tell the income tax about all of it? What about when you were Mate? Did you never sell any old ropes or canvas or condemned paint? This whisky we've been drinking. Will that go through on your personal account or will it come off that huge entertainment allowance the company gives us to make port officials friendly? I could go on all night. You know all the angles as well as I do. Maybe better. You've been at it longer. And when it was easier. No, Commodore, you're no more honest than the next man and that's not very. So the next time you're feeling upset about my sex life you just remember how I feel about all the people who go around stealing."

Lang had sat through the whole tirade in silence. He was very angry but he was pleased he had kept himself in control. "That was a very long speech, Captain. It must have tired you as much as it tired me. I suggest we both turn in now. We've got to take this ship to sea tomorrow. We should be properly rested for that."

"Right you are." He stood up. "Thanks for the chat. And the drinks. I'll be back aboard at daybreak." He made for the door. Silly old crow. Takes everything so seriously. Took every word of that as a personal insult. Why doesn't he join in and let his hair down and call me some dirty words instead of just sitting there with a face like fizz.

"Captain Stock."

"Yes."

"I didn't hear you correctly, did I. You didn't say you were going ashore."

"No, I said I'd be back on board at daybreak. But of course to get back on board I'll have first of all to go ashore."

Lang walked across the room past his staff captain and peered into the alleyway. Then he closed the door and came back into the room. "Captain, I've tried very hard to be reasonable tonight. I've tried to make allowances for all the strain and tension of the trials. It has not been easy. You have pushed me very hard. As we are about to start a voyage tomorrow let me remind you of something. I am in command of this ship. I intend to command it. The fact that you are yourself one of the company's captains does not entitle you to make your own rules. Nor does the fact that you are an expert on this ship and its equipment. Nor even does the fact that you may feel you should have had this command yourself. You accepted the post you now hold. At the risk of seeming coarse, I might say that you've made your bed, now you must lie in it."

Stock summoned up a grim smile. "In the context, Commodore, that's funnier than you think. I hadn't realised it was all going to be so formal. I apologise. Now, I have a pressing engagement ashore. Do I have your permission to go?"

"No, sir, you do not. And what's more, if your pressing engagement was with Miss Odinoku, it's as well you don't go."

"What does that mean?" snapped Mike.

Lang turned away and sat down. "It means, Captain, that this evening I took it upon myself to do something I should have done a long time ago. I talked to Miss Odinoku before she left. I thanked her for all the wonderful work she has done for the ship and the crew. I then told her that, for her sake, I was glad that we were leaving. I told her it would be tragic if a young woman in her prime was to develop an attachment for a man of another race, and a married man at that. I told her I hoped she would settle down happily in her own country. And I told her I would use all my influence to ensure that you did not soon return to Japan."

Stock did not take it all in at first. Then he laughed harshly. "Well, bully for you, Lang. She must have been very impressed."

"Yes, I'm glad to say she was. She was upset of course. But she'll get over it. She's made of strong stuff."

It was a moment or two before Mike put it all together in his mind. Then it gelled in a great mass of disgust. He spoke slowly, precisely, quietly, venomously. "You stupid old bastard. You mealy mouthed prude. No, don't get up. Please don't get up. Just sit there, then I won't have to hit you." He stepped across and stood over Lang in his chair. "You don't know a thing, do you. You're all white and shining outside, and inside you're like a stinking sewer. Well, that's fine by me till you start spilling your filth over other people. Now you listen, Lang, and listen good. I'm going ashore. Now I've got to go. I've got to go to find out what you've done. Shut up. I'll tell you something you don't know. You don't know the date. You don't know the date 'cause you don't know about marking calendars. But I do. And it's a bad date for that woman. It's also the last night she's going to see me for a long time. That made it a worse day. And your little speech must have completed the hellishness. She's a Jap, that girl. Don't you know about Japs, Lang? You were here for years in the war. Don't you know what Japs do when they get ashamed, when they feel their honour's gone? I'll tell you. They get down on their knees and they take a bloody big knife in their hands and they carve their guts out. Think about that, Lang." He turned away and strode to the door. He pulled it open and stepped through.

He was going to slam it shut behind him when he saw the commodore in his chair. He was unnaturally still. He was staring straight ahead. It was as if the old man had been frozen where he sat. Stock let go of the handle and the door swung open. He stepped back inside and went up to Lang. "Commodore. Commodore, can you hear me? Are you all right? Lang. Commodore. Come on, snap out of it." Stock pushed a hand inside the other man's shirt. God, he can't be dead. No, there's a heart beat. Fast too, Very fast. He pulled the tie loose. "Come on, Lang, what the hell's happened. Snap out of it."

The eyes were open, wide open, but unseeing. I'll take a chance. He slapped at Lang's face, not hard, but time about with both hands. There was a flicker of reaction. Then he hit him. Hard with the open palm. That did it. It was if he had snapped the tension holding the old man's body. He went suddenly limp then sat up and peered about.

"Take it easy, sir. It's me. It's Stock, sir. You seemed to have some sort of black-out. How d'you feel?"

Lang looked around the cabin carefully. He looked at Mike. He looked down at himself in the chair. "I'm—I'm all right, Captain. What happened?"

"I don't know. We were having a bit of a row. Then you went sort of stiff all over. Can I get you anything?"

"No, no, I'll be all right. Just tiredness, I suppose." He remembered now. Maybe it was just tiredness. He was certainly tired. But it was Stock's talk of the knife and hara-kiri that had cut him off from his cabin, his ship, his staff captain. He had suddenly seen that penthouse on top of the hotel. He had remembered what Yashawa had said. He had seen the frail old invalid in the wheelchair. He had seen him with that ornamental dagger in both hands, the blade already through the silk jacket and buried in the old man's body. He had seen a suicide the Japanese way but he had seen it as a murder. And Lang had seen himself as the murderer.

"Should I send ashore for a doctor?" It was Stock.

"No, no, Captain. Don't let's make a song and dance about nothing. I'm fine now. Just tired. I remember now. We had a bit of a set to."

"I'm sorry about that, sir."

Lang got to his feet and tried a few steps across the room. "See, I'm fine."

Mike shook his head. "You certainly seem to be. I thought you'd had a stroke or something. You had me worried."

"I may be getting on, Captain, but I'm not ready for the

131

next world yet. Now, didn't you say something about going ashore?"

"Well, I had planned to but . . ."

"But nothing. You go ahead. I'm all right. You can see that. I'll see you in the morning."

"O.K. If you're sure."

"I'm sure. And keep quiet about this, Stock, if you don't mind." Lang smiled. That was a surprise. He was not a man who smiled often.

CHAPTER ELEVEN

The *Emperor* sailed at nine in the morning.

Kim watched it go from the balcony of Mr. Yashawa's penthouse. The sun was already well up over the sea. Its light shone and sparkled over the calm water of the bay. It was the kind of day that would be very hot, and later the clouds would build into huge thunderheads and towards evening the rain would come in a slashing deluge and the twilight would be wet and cool. But now in the morning it was an idyllic scene. Kim looked because she could not help herself but she felt no involvement with the ship down in the bay. It was just a ship weighing anchor and heading out to sea. It happened all the time. The ship was bigger than ever before but it was just a ship. She knew that her Mike-san was there, probably up in that glass encircled bridge that winked and flashed as it caught and reflected the sunlight. That did not seem important. He was not going away now. He had been gone since first light; since that last kiss, that last caressing chuck under the chin. He had been gone in that resolute way of his, sliding back the door of their room, walking away down the corridor, never looking back. "Never look back." It was a favourite saying of his. "Never look back." It was the way he did everything. He would be doing it now as the anchor chain clanked in and the ship swung her great bulk round to head away into the Pacific. He would be sitting up there in the bridge, his eyes scanning dials, his fingers ready to close switches and pull levers, his ears cocked to every sound, every report. He would not look back, not at the harbour or the town, or the hill or the tower on which she stood. It was a good thing to do, not to look back. But looking back was all that Kim had left to hold on to. The future frightened her.

She shivered. Even on a hot day there was always a gusting breeze at the top of the tower block. She saw white on the water under the ship's stern. It grew and spread then suddenly lengthened and became a wake. The *Emperor* was under way. The boom of the siren drifted back over the town. Five long blasts. Kim did not see the ship now. Instead she saw all the good times she had had with Mike. The bus trips, the picnics, the sightseeing. Swimming, climbing, running on the beach, Kim always ahead and shouting back that the exercise was good for his figure. Eating, dancing, holding hands in the theatre. Talking, not talking, just being in the same place together, alone, making love. She had a lot to remember.

But the closest memory was the night before. She remembered it minute by minute. There was much of it she wished she could forget. The old commodore. He meant well, of course. He was trying to be kind. I don't suppose he knew how I would take it. I don't suppose he knew that he made me feel like a cheap tart from down there in the town. A Japanese tart, a whore of another race and another colour, trying to steal a white man away from his white wife. Yes, he meant well with all his simple rubbish about settling down in my own country and marrying one of my own people. It's all so easy when you have just a few simple rules. Maybe love, my kind of love for Mike, is all a romantic myth but it's real to me. It's not simple. And when I broke down and cried, there on the ship's deck, in public, he didn't understand. He was sympathetic, he patted me on the head like a lap dog and said it would all come right in the end. He didn't know I was crying for being made ashamed of something I was proud of, crying because I was ashamed of breaking down in front of a stranger, crying because he said he was going to make sure that Mike would never come back. Poor old Commodore Lang. He's like all old people, full of advice. And if the advice hurts, then it's good advice, for suffering is good. It's not, it's hell. It's hell like old people are hell, crowding round, advising, cajoling, protecting, hurting. Stifling, smothering. Parents, teachers, Lang, old Mr. Yashawa.

And then he told Mike. That only made it worse, for Mike was not himself when he came to our room. He was sort of withdrawn, worried about the commodore. More worried about the commodore than about me, about us on our last night together. We talked about it. He and Lang had rowed about me. Lang had had some sort of attack. Mike said he'd never seen anything like it. He felt responsible. He felt it was his fault. And I was furious because he was thinking about that silly old man, not about me. And for the first time I hated Mike. I hated him for meeting me, and wooing me, and loving me, and giving me happiness. It got better after that. It was as if we had needed to hate ourselves and each other just for a few moments to remember how much we were in love. Not equally in love. I've always known that. He's not the exclusive type. Maybe men aren't. The ones like Mike love their work the same way they love women. One woman in one place isn't enough for them. That's all right if I don't know about them, don't have to compete with them. All that matters is that he comes back.

Will he come back? He says he will, maybe sooner than I

think. The commodore said he wouldn't. The commodore said he'd use his influence. Other people might use their influence too. Old Mr. Yashawa might. He's not out here beside me. For him that ship's already gone and Mike with it. Yes, he might use his influence. But it won't matter. Mike will be back and it'll all start again and I'll know how it will end. But every so often I'll have to take hold of myself and tell myself not to pray that something happens to his wife so he'll be free. That would be no answer anyway. There are his children, these two girls. He's conscientious. He wouldn't desert them. He wouldn't take them home a new Japanese mother. No, I just want him to come back and go on coming back till he doesn't need me and I don't need him and I hope that's never.

The ship was well clear of the bay and going away fast. It was stern on, suddenly quite small. Kim turned her back on the sea. Through the windows of the penthouse she could see Mr. Yashawa at his desk. That was the Japanese way. Discipline by the industrious example. Kim knew what she would do. She would go down to her office and work and work and work. There would be that first cruel moment when she found the bunch of flowers and the note Mike had sent. She would cry a little, hating him for prolonging her agony, loving him for not having forgotten. Then she would work. She stepped across the balcony to the penthouse door. She wanted to take one last look out to sea. No. Never look back.

She went in and stood beside the old man. There was a smile on his face. On his desk was a single sheet of paper. On it he had written in elegant brush strokes, "Tell Commodore Lang." The bottle of pain-killing tablets was there. It was empty. Mr. Yashawa was dead.

It was almost eleven o'clock when Stock came off the bridge. He had handed over to the normal forenoon watch as soon as the ship was clear of the bay. He had stayed on at the console in

one of the spare chairs, just watching. The Chief had wanted to
ease her up to service speed. That took an hour. Then they
switched to bridge control of the engines and engaged the auto-
pilot. The *Emperor* was on her own. There was a fascination
about sitting at the control console. Even with all the months
of training, it would take a bit of getting used to. Just sitting
there seeing all the information being gathered and digested
and acted on and recorded, all without the raising of a finger.
A few queries came in on the intercom from various parts of
the ship. Nothing important. Just what could be expected on
the first day out. Where's such and such? What d'you want
done with this and that?

Mike stayed longer on the bridge than he need have done.
His fascination with the ship and its gear gave way to a fascination with the commodore. There had been no time to talk
when he got back on board. Just time to ask Lang if he was all
right. He said he was. And so it seemed.

Just the thrill of getting to sea at last, Mike told himself.
Don't suppose the old boy's ever been so long ashore since he
served his time. No, that's not right. Not since he was in that
Jap prison camp during the war. More than three years that
time. Wonder what went on then. Never talks about it. Got a
gong for it though. Must have had a rough time. I suppose
these fingers tell some of the story. They say the Japs had a
thing about fingers and toes. Ugh. He came through it all
pretty well. Look at him now. He's strutting up and down that
bridgefront like a cockerel in a new hen run. Couldn't care less
about this box of tricks. He doesn't even know it's here doing
everyone's job. All he sees is the sea through the windows and
all he feels is the matting under his feet. He's a real old romantic. One of the all-I-ask-is-a-tall-ship school. I wonder though.
He's almost too much the shipmaster this morning. I'll have to
keep an eye on him. That business last night still worries me.
He went out as if I'd snapped a switch on him. But he came

out of it so quickly and with no ill effects. It was as if it wasn't physical at all. His mind? No. Not Lang. He's so sane it's almost comical. Come on, Mike. Jerk yourself out of it. It's yourself you're sorry for. Too long ashore. Too long with Kim. Poor kid. Wonder how she is?

He got to his feet and tapped the watch officer on the shoulder. "You're on your own, lad. I'm off for a cuppa."

"Right, sir. I think I'm going to like this ship. Very relaxing."

Stock grinned and clambered down to the bridgefront. The commodore did not notice him. Lang was walking his bridge.

Sonia hailed Stock as he came down on to the lower bridge. "Good morning, Captain. You're looking very serious this morning. Nothing wrong, I hope."

Mike shook his head. "No, nothing wrong, Mrs. North. But we're at sea now, you know. I've put on my serious ship-mastering face. It goes with the uniform."

She laughed. "It doesn't suit you. Take it off."

"At once, sir." He grinned.

"That's better. Now will you make me a promise?"

"Maybe."

"Will you never call me Mrs. North again. My name's Sonia."

He pretended to think for a minute. "Yes, I think I can promise that. On two conditions."

"And they are?"

"One, that you call me Mike."

"Done."

"And two, that you assure me that Gene won't fire me for familiarity."

"Why should he? You're joking of course. You call him Gene."

"He doesn't like it though. Not really."

"Nonsense. He tells everyone to call him Gene."

"I know that. What I said was that he doesn't like it. Don't deny it, Sonia. I know. I can tell. His passport may say he's American but his manners are British. Better class British, of course. He likes to be shown a little respect by the serfs. A bit of cap-doffing, forelock-pulling, that sort of thing."

Sonia smiled. "I don't think he'd think you were being very respectful now."

"No, but he'll never know, will he."

"He might get to hear."

"Then I'll call you Mrs. North for ever and a day."

She put up her hands. "No, not that. Please, not that."

They both laughed.

"Where is he anyway?" asked Mike. "He should be out here revelling in the smell and sound of the sea."

"He was. He saw his big new ship safely out of port then decided he had work to do. He's like that. He believes in work."

"But I thought this was to be a sort of holiday."

"It is. But Gene always does some work, every day."

"I see. A sort of sop to his millionaire's conscience."

Sonia was serious. "Don't let's fall out, Mike; not on the first day of the trip. Oh, I know you're the kind who thinks no one's any good unless he's pulled himself up by his bootstraps. Believe me, it can be pretty tough being a millionaire. Some of the bootstrap brigade have had it a lot easier."

"I dare say. I'm sorry. You mustn't take me too seriously. Of course I'm a terribly serious person. But I try to be funny to cover it up. My humour's often in pretty bad taste."

"Oh, I don't know. I think you're funny most of the time."

Mike grinned. "That puts me in my place. Let's change the subject."

"Yes, let's. You went ashore last night, didn't you. How was Kim?"

138

He looked at her. "I can see we're both prone to a bit of bad taste. No, no, don't apologise. She's fine. Not hilarious about my leaving. Neither am I for that matter. But needs must. I'll be back in a few months."

"It's pretty big between you two, isn't it."

"Pretty." He shook his head. "But don't you worry, Sonia. I've been a sailor for a long time. I know how to make do." He beckoned to her and she leaned forward. "How would you like to come and see my etchings?"

She smiled. "Your funny side's showing again. Remember, I'm not your type."

"That's true. I forgot. How about a cup of coffee then?"

"That I'll settle for."

They went round the house and down to the smoke room.

Gene North was working. He was at the desk in their day cabin writing up his journal. He had kept it going for years. It was not a diary. It had started as an ideas book. Every time he heard something interesting, or thought of some new way of doing anything, he wrote it down. Then as the habit grew he started to include impressions of the people he met, stories he heard of other people, colourful phrases, anything that intrigued him. Sometimes he'd ask his journal a question, then answer it from as many points of view as possible. It had long been an important part of his life. Not only was it a storehouse of information, it also served to restrain him when he felt an especial enthusiasm for a person or a project. Then he would pick up one of the volumes at random and skip through it. It never failed to surprise him how often he had had to change his attitude to a new idea or his feeling about some person. There were several dozen thick, neatly written journals locked away at home in New York. Even with the libellous bits edited out, they would have brought any publisher the non-fiction award of the year. Gene North moved in high places.

But Gene also moved at other levels. He wrote about what

was happening round him each day. That day, he was writing about the *Emperor* and the men to do with her.

"We are now at sea and I have time to collect my thoughts. The ship came through yesterday's trials with flying colours. All the planning and training (and the attendant expense) seem to have been fully justified. If the other parts of Project Emperor turn out as well as this ship, the whole scheme will be an immense success. I must send Jim Bruce a cable on these lines as it is very much his project and he deserves the bulk of the credit not only for conceiving it but for seeing it through. I had confirmation from him yesterday that the new loading point in the Gulf will be ready for the *Emperor* when she gets there after this first trip to the West Coast. I suppose it's as well to show the ship off over there as there is time to spare till the Gulf and the U.K. terminals are ready—it will certainly give the ship and crew time to shake down—but I can't help disapproving in principle of running a ship representing this capital outlay, without cargo, the only benefit being an elusive advantage in public relations. Must get some figures on this to beat Jim over the head with.

About Jim. I was concerned when I arrived in Japan to hear a rumour (from Captain Stock) that he, Jim, might be negotiating with other interests. I am still waiting to hear from my sources if there is any substance in this. He must, of course, have had approaches. He's not the kind of man one meets every day of life. I would have thought he would have confided in me. Unless he has been tempted. I refuse to think about it any more until I get a report on whom he has been meeting recently. I suspect the whole thing is one of Stock's childish jokes. He apparently admitted as much to Sonia the other evening. I suppose it's in character for him to try and pull my leg. It is to be hoped that he doesn't pull it once too often.

Stock is an interesting character though. One of the new

type of seamen. Strongly opposed to the traditions of the sea, a technologist and a manager rather. He certainly seems to be extraordinarily competent but I would like to see a greater maturity in a man with his responsibilities. His attitude tends to be flippant in the face of authority, an odd stand to take when one is in a position of authority oneself. He was enjoying (I suppose that's the right word) a long standing affair in Japan with a charming young woman employed by the shipyard. He made no attempt to keep it a secret but this very fact suggests a disdain for discipline which could prove unfortunate in a man charged with imposing it on others. He is married in England, apparently happily, though that seems a little odd in the circumstances. No, on second thoughts, I should not condemn him on these grounds. He does do an outstanding job of work and that should be my only concern.

Oddly enough, the officers and men seem to work very well under his leadership. I suppose his competence gains their respect and his human failings only make him seem more one of them. There does now seem to be a type of leadership like this. I prefer the old style with its hard distinction between managers and men. It seems less liable to failure. But I suppose this all means that I'm getting old. It may also mean that I am an American with a great feeling for the European way of doing things. I just can't believe it's good for children and parents to be friends, if that means that the parents have to act like children and smile cheerfully as the house is wrecked around them. The analogy holds good in business. No, Stock certainly has an excellent record here but I would like to see more steel in him. If only he could do something about his appearance. He looks like a friendly uncle from out of town. Kids dote on him; parents live in terror of his next visit. That's good. Yes, that seems to sum him up.

Come to think of it, Stock's ability and Commodore Lang's appearance would make a formidable blend.

No, that's unfair to Lang. I think I misjudged him when I met him in Japan. It's always a problem to distinguish between respect and obsequiousness. Or rather it's a problem to decide what induces a show of respect. Is it a feeling for social position or status in a business or profession? Is it fear for one's job or a feeling of inadequacy? Is it a crude attempt to ingratiate oneself? With Lang, I thought it might be a certain awe in the presence of one of the bosses from New York. It may have been that but I now feel sure he was ill at ease only because he was, quite literally, not in his element. Lang's element is the sea and ships. The change in him since taking the *Emperor* on trials, and particularly since sailing this morning, has been truly remarkable. His whole bearing, the look in his eyes, the set of his jaw, all have been transformed simply by leaving the land behind. Of course, he's had more than forty years of it. I suppose he feels the land as insubstantial under his feet as a bad sailor feels the deck of a ship.

I said that this change was particularly noticeable this morning. I wonder if that might have anything to do with something I happened to see last evening. I was out on deck taking a breath of air. Some sort of argument seemed to be going on in the commodore's quarters. I could make nothing of it but now and again voices were raised. Eventually Stock came out on deck and went down below. He was not his usual ebullient self. He seemed chastened. I can only assume that he overstepped the mark with the commodore and was put firmly in his place. That would be in character for both of them. Good for old Lang. I'm glad he showed his mettle. Must make a note to tell Jim that his favourites are not perfect when faced with good ones of the old school. It would be interesting to see Stock and Lang together in a real emergency. I know who would have my money. Pity it won't ever happen. These new ships are too safe for that kind of thing. Jim and his Research Unit have thought of everything. Just as well. Forty million dollars is a lot of money to have floating about the ocean.

Interesting as the ship and the two captains are, the most interesting person on board is, of course, Sonia. This marriage is really working. I'm amazed. I had begun to think that marriage was inevitably disappointing. More men should marry their secretaries. A few years together in an office is an eminently better preparation than any engagement. She's really looking forward to the trip. She has a great capacity for enjoying simple pleasures. I'm looking forward to it too. We'll be together more than we have been. And she's right about my overdoing things. All this jet travel and the time changes and the meetings and receptions and parties on an impossibly tight schedule play hell with me nowadays. Yes, this trip will be a proper holiday."

CHAPTER TWELVE

Kim's cable arrived just after noon. It was short. "Mr. Yashawa is dead."

The commodore was in his day room when the Sparks brought it down. Stock was there. They were having the first of the prescribed daily management meetings. The chief engineer had asked to be excused on this first day at sea; he was fully engaged playing broody hen to his complicated clutch of equipment.

Lang read the message and sat quite still, trying to take it in. He saw at once that terrifying picture of the night before. He saw the old man plunging that dagger into his bowels. He looked at the cable again. It read to him like an accusation.

It might as well have run on; "And you killed him." He shook his head.

"Bad news?" It was Stock.

The commodore looked up. His mouth was dry. "It's Mr. Yashawa. He's dead."

"Too bad. But he was pretty old, wasn't he? And an invalid."

"I suppose so. It's a shock though. I didn't expect it."

"I don't suppose he did either." Lang did not notice the flippancy. "Why'd they tell you?" Stock went on. "You only met him once, didn't you?"

Lang nodded. "Yes, just once. Just once." He was staring past the other man. The message form was lying on the desk where it had fallen from his hand.

Mike reached over and picked it up. "I see it's from Kim. She'll be upset. She had a soft spot for the old boy." He put the cable back on the desk. He peered at it then smiled. "That's funny. Just realised how appropriate her initials are."

Lang looked round. "Sorry, what was that?"

"I was talking about Kim's initials. K.O. Very appropriate. K.O. Knockout. You know. Old Yashawa."

The commodore crinkled his brow and moved his eyes from Stock to the cable. When he looked up his eyes were blazing with anger. "Get out of here," he said quietly and deliberately. "Get out." This time he roared.

Stock was startled by the venom in Lang's voice. "All right. It's not the end of the world, you know. Maybe we can get round to running this ship when you come out of mourning."

"Get out," bellowed Lang. He stood gripping the edge of the desk till the other man had gone. Then he sat down slowly and tried to think about that message. At first he could not think about anything but his revulsion for Stock. Try as he might to see the man's qualities, something always happened to remind him that Stock was cast in the same mould that Lang had grown up hating. In Mike Stock, the commodore thought he recognised the father he could barely remember.

John Lang had last seen his father in 1914. He was five then. The old John Lang never came home from that war. He could have come home. He lived through it. He never came home because he did not want to. Home to him was a nagging wife and a snotty-nosed child. Home to him was rent and house-keeping money and new curtains and shoes for the kid. He had better things to do with his money. There was beer and rum and brag and solo and women. In a town full of sailors, reports of him came from time to time from door to door along the grimy street where the boy and his mother lived. She could have tried to keep them from him. She could have said his father had died in the war. But Mrs. Lang was a bitter woman. She had good cause. It was no easy matter to bring up a child decently at that time in that place with nothing but what she could earn scrubbing floors and taking in washing and mending. Young John grew up knowing his father as a lecher, a drunk and a scoundrel. It was a harsh portrait but the facts were true enough. Old John Lang was really a boy who never grew up. He was a good seaman. He made bosun more than once. It was never long before he was back as an A.B., or out of a job. He was given to punching people, particularly officers.

Young John went to sea as a deck boy. It was the bottom of the ladder but his mother knew he would climb it. She had spent a lot of time teaching him the rules and disciplines that would take him there. They took him there. By the mid-1930's he had his master's certificate. He was already in tankers. He had been since his first job as third mate. Tankers paid better and he had had his mother to repay. On the way up he had seen men like his father. He despised them. As an officer he had seen more men like that. He had pushed them to the limit. You could do that in the thirties. There were a lot of men after very few jobs.

It was different now. Ships were changing. Everything was changing. Age and experience no longer meant much, except maybe that they branded you as out-of-date. All that seemed to matter now was the new button-pushing technology. Instinct was discounted, electronic wizardry was at a premium. Lang had long ago recognised the new pattern. He recognised it but he excepted himself from it. He was an old dog and he did not mean to learn many new tricks. He had learned his seamanship in a previous generation. He believed that basic truths about basic things like the sea could never change. He might never be able to prove it but for the little time left to him he was going to hold on to what he had spent his life learning.

Thinking about the little time left to him reminded him suddenly that time had run out for old Mr. Yashawa. And time had maybe run out for him because he, Lang, had nursed an old hate and convinced a tired old man that he was someone he was not, someone who owed a debt which could only be repaid by giving his life. The commodore shivered and shook his head. That's not true. I told him time and again that he wasn't Kuno. Hold on there. Why am I taking it for granted that he committed suicide? Because I had a sort of vision. That's silly. That was just in my mind, imagined. He was old, he was an invalid. He had a stroke last year. It's more than likely he had another. The cable just said he was dead. Nothing about suicide. That cable. Why was it sent? Why was I told? I had only met him once. True, we had both started to wonder if our paths had crossed before. But only we knew that. He would never have told anyone else about that. No, not even Miss Odinoku. So she must have been told to send that cable. She must have been told by him. And if she was told by him, he must have known he was going to die. Maybe he did just have another stroke and was conscious long enough to tell her. No. I know that's not how it was. I just seem to know. He told

146

her because he knew he was going to die. And he knew he was going to die because he had decided to kill himself. Maybe he had even decided before I met him. Why? Because he thought he might have been Kuno? No. Just because he was old and in great pain. He said as much. He was always in pain and had thought about ending his life. He told me. He even asked me how I thought he would do it. With that ornamental dagger, the traditional Japanese way; or with an overdose of pills. That's odd. I feel I know how he did it. I'm sure. It was with the pills.

I can check on that. I can cable back and ask. No. There's no need. I know. He took an overdose of these pills. He was old and in pain. He could no longer take an active part in the business he'd built from nothing; he just wanted to die. But why to-day? Why not yesterday, or last week? Of course, that's why he wanted me to know. He waited because he wanted to meet me and have me tell him he had not been Kuno. He wanted to meet me and tell me about that woman who was never killed. He wanted to be at peace himself and put my mind at rest before he died. He did that too. Since I met him all my hate for Kuno seems to have drained away. I don't even think about him or about my hands. Maybe I regret all these years of imagined guilt, all these sleepless nights and terrifying dreams. But that's in the past now; finally. Now there's just that medal to give the lie to my heroism. I'll send it back. That's what I'll do. I'll send it back and say I don't want it any more. No. That would be silly. That would do no good. No, that medal's not a public thing. It's private, for me to sort out myself. I've only got a few months to go. Then there'll be no uniform, no medal ribbons. It will be as if I never had it.

Lang got up from his desk and walked across the cabin. He stopped and stared out along the foredeck of his ship. He felt suddenly happier than he could remember. He was puzzled;

it was an odd feeling to follow so closely on news of death. But he felt he understood it. Mr. Yashawa was happy in death, released from pain. Lang was happy in what he saw as the old man's gift of a new freedom. He was happy too to be at sea again, Japan astern, never to be seen again, his huge ship ploughing ahead into the Pacific. His ship. The commodore's ship.

His pride straightened his shoulders. Old dog maybe, he told himself, but I won this. He went over to the phone and invited the Norths for drinks before lunch.

It was all quiet at Phoenix Island. No flames flickered in the crater, no lava surged out and ran down to hiss into the sea and become land. It was as if the new island was resting before the next stage in gestation.

The island lay alone in the vastness of the ocean. No navy ship now sat in attendance. There was no point. No one else was interested in Phoenix. Aircraft checked it as part of their regular patrols. The island was a long term prospect as a base. The initial enthusiasm for this gift from nature had waned. Ideas changed quickly in defence policy. Money and resources were strained to keep pace with immediate needs. Phoenix Island was an ace in the hole. It was encouraging to know it was there. It was a relief to know it was not costing anything.

CHAPTER THIRTEEN

The *Emperor* was four days out into the Pacific when it all started happening.

Till then the ocean had lived up to its name. Winds varied from light airs to a stiff breeze but nothing more. The sea followed the wind from oily calms through ruffles to a vista of white horses from horizon to horizon. The one unchanging factor was the swell. It was long, very long. It was proof of the vastness of this unobstructed stretch of water. It was also proof of the ferocity the weather could achieve; fierce enough to bequeath this permanent symbol of its power. The weather reports told of a new typhoon sweeping up through the China Sea. It was following a normal path. It would blow itself out long before it caught up with the *Emperor*. But by then it would already have added its contribution to the ever present swell.

Smaller ships often found this swell uncomfortable. It was so long that they had to mount the rising slope to the crest and slide down into the trough only to face another slope. It was not a violent motion, rather the opposite. But its constancy, day after day for thousands of miles, could be wearing on the nerves. The *Emperor*'s immense length overcame this. She could span three crests in a swell as long as six hundred feet. She moved across the undulating surface, not conforming to its shape. Such movement as there was was damped down and almost eliminated by the new expansion joint midships.

In these first few days, Mike Stock had varied the water ballast all the time to test the system and compare the results with the figures from the test tank experiments ashore. The

ever-present swell had given more data. Stock was not alto-
gether happy with the figures. They checked out. There was
nothing in them he could put his finger on as being wrong.
There were minute differences in reaction time between the
test tank figures and the readings he was getting at sea. They
were small enough to be written off as insignificant. But they
nagged at him. If they were not insignificant, then multiplied
under extreme conditions of stress they could spell big trouble.
He told himself they were of no importance. He told himself he
was worrying about them just because the commodore had said
before the launching that he was unhappy with the joint. He
told himself that the readings were only a sign of the teething
troubles of any new system working itself in. He told himself
that even if they did mean something, the extremes needed to
produce any real danger were unheard of and therefore impossible. He told no one. What Lang did not know about, he could
not nark about. Stock kept quiet and went on collecting and
collating readings every few hours.

Apart from that midship joint, he was happy with the ship.
She was running in well. He was busy and that kept him from
brooding about Kim. It had surprised him to realise there was
a danger of his brooding about her. Their only contact since
the *Emperor* sailed had been after the news of old Yashawa's
death. Mike had sent her flowers; not a wreath, just flowers
for herself. That was how he felt about death. The dead were
dead; the important people were those who were left behind.
There had been no acknowledgement. He did not expect one.
But he did find he was thinking a lot about Kim. It helped
to talk it over with Sonia.

"I don't know why you're surprised, Mike. I didn't see the
two of you together much but the only thing that surprises me
is that you're surprised. I could see you were both in over your
heads."

"As obvious as that, was it?"

"To me it was. Didn't you realise?"

"Sort of. It was pretty special. But then I've had special sorts of things before. I always managed to slam the door on them."

"But you're not trying to slam the door on this one. You're going back there soon. You want to take up where you left off. Isn't that so?"

"I suppose it is. You disapprove, don't you?"

"No. I don't disapprove; I don't approve. There are more than enough people around interfering in things that aren't any of their business. But I'm intrigued. I don't think I've met anyone just like you before. Oh, I've met plenty of misunderstood husbands. New York's full of them. I suppose any city is. I've just never met anyone who's as frank as you about it or who can make it all sound so normal."

"It's simpler my way. You don't have to keep remembering what story you've told each person. You just tell them all the truth, some more than others. This time, things have got out of hand. It's like on a tanker, when you get contamination."

"How's that?"

"Well, if you're carrying more than one type of oil, you have to get what the manual calls sectional segregation. In other words you have to make sure there's no chance of one product mixing with another. You do it by splitting the ship into sections, each sealed off from the others. It's like in life. One section knows there are other sections, but if there's no contact there's no contamination. I know it might not work for everyone but it's always worked for me."

"It's an original thought anyway, Mike. I've never thought of my life as being a tanker."

He nodded. "No, I don't suppose you have. How do you think, Sonia? Like a secretary or a woman or a wife?"

"Why not all three at the same time?"

"Why not indeed."

151

She took his arm and shook it. "Come on, Mike. Cheer up. All you need is time. Time cures everything."

He laughed. "Everyone says that. It doesn't, you know. It's time that causes all the trouble in the first place. Especially with women."

"Go on," said Sonia. "Don't leave me in mid-air. Tell me about time and women."

Mike smiled. "You're a prime case of what I mean. Nice, well-adjusted woman. Good to talk to. Got common sense. Good looking too but you don't wobble your eyes at everything in trousers. A pal. Just what every man needs. A sort of mother figure, sister figure, just to talk to."

"I hope I don't recognise myself."

"You won't. But that's you, for me, now. And I like you that way. But time would ruin all that. Given time, I'd start to like you a different way. Given time, sex would rear its delightful head."

"Is that so? Is there going to be enough time on this trip?"

"I doubt it. I certainly hope not. I've got problems enough."

Sonia shook her head and smiled. "You make it all sound so inevitable, Mike. What about the woman? Doesn't she have to feel something too? Let's be honest. You're not the most romantic looking man in the world."

"I know. Thank goodness for that. Don't you see how it works? Already you're off your guard. You've written me off as a danger. I wouldn't slim off my figure or try to stop myself going bald for all the tea in China. The way I look's my secret weapon."

"That's my cue to run along to the pool. Don't worry, Mike. You're like a rubber ball. You'll bounce back from anything."

The pool on the poop was Sonia's favourite place on the *Emperor*. She had quickly established a routine. She went along

152

there as soon as she got up in the morning and again between five and six in the afternoon. The water followed every small movement of the ship. It was better than a pool ashore. To lie and float was restful, relaxing, for the water moved her to and fro like a rocking cradle. Then one wave would catch up on the one before, bouncing back off the pool edge, and the splash would make her splutter and come upright and tread water. She would lie floating, her eyes shut, trying to guess when the waves would meet and swamp her. It was fun. It was solitary fun though. No one else ever came near the pool when she was there. That surprised her. On passenger ships, one girl near a pool soon attracted a crowd. Passenger ships were obviously different. Here she was aware all the time she was a woman. There were two reactions from the officers and men. They either stared at her with frank interest or looked the other way when she was near. She could understand both attitudes. She knew too why they stayed away from the pool. It had to do with who she was. Mrs. North could be greeted on deck, shown round the ship, joked with in the dining saloon. But Mrs. North could not be greeted or joked with when she was in a bathing suit in the pool. Silly. But after the first two days she was quite pleased at having the water to herself. Away from there it was difficult to be alone even though the ship was so big. There was always someone ready to show her some new wonder, or invite Gene and her for coffee or drinks, or ask them to join in a game of cards.

These first few days were certainly full with seeing over the ship. Her quick tour on her first day in Japan had shown her nothing. Now the Chief Engineer tried to explain the complexities of the engine room to her, the Sparks sat her down in the wireless room and showed her all the wonders of his wireless gear, Mike told her all about the bridge and the operations room and how a tanker worked. The chef told her about the food. That fascinated Sonia more than anything else. The first

half-dozen menus had convinced her she would have to watch
her weight, even if the trip was only about twelve days. It was
like dining in a five star hotel, except that the portions were
bigger. Until the chef got his turn to instruct her in the secrets
of his department, she could not understand how so much
wonderful food came out of such a tiny galley. Even when she
knew the secret, she found it difficult to believe. All the food
had been prepared in Britain weeks before. It was deep frozen
after cooking and shipped to Japan in special containers. Deep
down in the *Emperor*'s deep freeze was enough food to keep the
whole crew feeding like gourmets for the next nine months.
There was an infinite choice. You chose from a menu half an
hour before each mealtime, and by the time you sat down the
food had come up from the deep freeze, gone through the
special ovens and there it was in front of you, complete with
sauces and garnish. And it was not just the steak and kidney
pie type of thing. Duck, turkey, fried chicken, chicken Mary-
land, mixed grills, weiner schnitzels, omelettes, steaks (rare,
medium, or well done); they were all there, and more besides.
The catering staff was half what it was on a ship one tenth the
size. That saved a lot of money. And the food was all bought at
competitive prices in Britain by Inoco. No kickbacks to chief
stewards or captains. And no complaints about the feeding.
Like everything else on the *Emperor*, the catering had been
through the searching scrutiny of Bruce's Research Unit.

Sonia also liked the strict timetable of shipboard life. The
same things happened at the same time each day. There were
Lang's little formal occasions. At half past noon she went with
Gene to the commodore's cabin. He greeted them as if he had
not seen them for months, checked his watch, peered through a
porthole, said "Well, I think the sun's well up over the yard-
arm," and served drinks. It was true what Gene said. The
commodore was a different man on board his ship, at sea. He
was still a bit stiff and formal but he was good company. He

could be quite gay. He had a fund of stories about ships and sailors. They were quite funny. Never in the slightest way bawdy. At half past six in the evening there was another little occasion. Lang would say something like, "It's sundown, lady and gentlemen, or if it's not it should be." Mike was sometimes there, not always. He always seemed to be restrained in Lang's company. Gene's got a theory about it. He thinks Mike and Lang had a row before we sailed. He claims the commodore put Mike in his place. Seems unlikely but he's certainly not himself at these little parties. He's not a drinker of course. But that can't be it. They're very sober occasions. Why don't I ask him what it's all about? I just don't. That's funny. It's as if that's one thing I don't want to hear from him. Silly. The commodore's just not Mike's type. It's as simple as that. He is the commodore and Mike isn't going to row with him in front of Gene and me. That'll be it.

Lang had noticed his staff captain's new reserve. He was pleased. He took it as proof of what he had always believed; that Stock, at sea, under the running discipline of a ship, would be much less of a thorn in his flesh than he had been all these months ashore. It never occurred to him that Stock might be harbouring any doubts about the ship. The *Emperor* was running smoothly and well. It certainly never occurred to him that his staff captain might be puzzled by the miraculous change in Lang himself since sailing from Japan. The commodore was aware of that change but it was what he had expected when the land was left behind and he was at sea again, at home. He alone knew that Mr. Yashawa, in life then in death, had unlocked for him the prison in which he had lived since the war. In the quiet of the night, alone, his lifelong discipline of doubt stirred and prodded him. Had he been right in his estimate of the circumstances of the old man's death? Should he have asked for details? Could it be that Yashawa had been Major Kuno? Had he made Yashawa kill himself? Was he a murderer? But John Lang had the puritan's capacity for self-deception. He felt better in himself than he had done for years. That was surely proof that his first feelings had been right. As for the doubts, he made sure he was never alone for too long. It was easy, with the Norths to be entertained. The commodore was enjoying this maiden voyage.

Gene North was another who was enjoying the voyage. He wrote at length in his journal about the *Emperor* as he discovered more and more of the novelty and complexity of the ship. He was generous in his praise and shrewd in his criticisms. He already had a list of costings he wanted to follow up when he got back to New York or London. Gene believed in technology. You had to in the oil business. But he also believed in dollars and cents. He knew that people with new ideas did not always follow his old fashioned rules of arithmetic. He also knew that sometimes you had to put money at risk to find new ways of making money. He saw it as one of his responsibilities, constantly to probe amid the spending to ensure that no one lost sight of the reason Inoco paid them.

But his real thrill was to see a brave new idea like the *Emperor* really working. "This is yet another justification of my long-held belief that directors and senior executives must, from time to time, get down from their pedestals and go out into the field to see the business at work. Whether it be a refinery in the middle of the desert or a ship in the middle of the ocean, it is out there that the best view of the company can be had. Figures and balance sheets can sometimes confuse but out in the field, away from the office, you can soon tell how things are going if you have the right kind of instinct. I suppose it dates me to say that I believe that the right kind of instinct is something some men have and that other men, regardless of universities and business schools, will never have."

There was one paragraph that marred his pleasure in the trip. "I have just received some intelligence on Stock's claim that Jim Bruce might be talking to other interests. I'm sure Stock made up the story as a joke but it now seems that it may turn out, in fact, to be less than funny. Jim has met Jock McAuslane three times in the past month. McAuslane has always recruited for his independent operations from the big companies but he has never before tried to catch as big a fish as Jim. I keep telling myself that Jim would not run out on Inoco; at least not without first trying to use any outside offer to improve his position with us. I keep telling myself that Jim is only taking the advice I gave him myself. Always listen to offers. You have nothing to lose by listening, and maybe a lot to gain, if only an insight into other people's operations. I hope I'm right. With Project Emperor now well and truly launched, Jim is in a very strong position."

On a more personal note he wrote: "It's good to see Sonia enjoying herself. As the only woman on board she is, of course, very popular. She seems to get the best out of everyone. It's a great talent in a woman. She gets on particularly well with Captain Stock. She tells me she teased him about his reputation as a lady killer and he replied that she wasn't his type. She says she was amused. I doubt it. Sonia is too much of a woman to be amused by that. But I must say that together they seem to behave rather like brother and sister. I think maybe I'm just a little jealous—he's much nearer her age than I am. An unworthy thought has just come to me. I'll write it down to get rid of it. Here it is. Sonia would never do anything that would risk losing me. Money and comfort mean too much to her. I'm disgusted with myself."

On the fourth night out from Japan the *Emperor* crossed the dateline eastbound.

The next morning, Mike met Sonia on the way back midships from her dip. "Good morning, Mrs. Millionaire. How are we this morning?"

"We're very upset."

"That's a pity. What's up?"

"It's the wrong day. That's what's up."

"Sorry. I'm not properly awake yet. Tell me."

"Surely you know. I woke up this morning and discovered it was yesterday again. It's ridiculous."

"Oh, that. Don't worry about that. When you're a big girl and have travelled a lot, the dateline won't worry you at all." He smiled at her.

"It's not funny. How d'you keep a diary when you have the same day twice running?"

"You keep a diary? Heavens, I'd better watch what I say."

"No, I don't keep a diary. But you know what I mean. It's all very confusing."

"It's not really. You lost a day flying to Japan. Now you're getting it back. That's fair."

"It's not the same. Losing a day didn't seem odd at all. Reliving a day I've already had, that's spooky."

"So time's an illusion."

"You can say that again. I sit there in my cabin of an evening and I look at the clock. It says eleven. Good. I've got time for an hour's reading. Then I look again and it's suddenly midnight and time to go to bed. And just because someone up there on the bridge has pressed a switch. I don't know how you stand it. It's like daylight saving happening every other night."

"You'll get to like it, Sonia. You'll miss it when you're back home in New York. You'll suddenly realise that time stands still there."

She laughed. "I'm sure I will. I'll certainly miss this ship. What a life. Why does anyone work in an office or a factory, Mike?"

"You wait. The sea's got teeth. You may be glad to get ashore."

"Never. It's all so marvellous. Not just the ship. The sea,

158

the space, the sky. Yes, the sky maybe most of all. It's full of newness all the time. It's never the same for more than a few seconds." She looked all around. Her eyes stopped wide out on the starboard bow. "Just look at that, Mike. Tell me true. Have you ever seen anything quite as lovely as that?"

He followed her pointing arm. That was newness for sure. It was so new its beauty was lost on him at first. It was so new it worried him.

CHAPTER FOURTEEN

The sky to the south east was a pale shimmering green. The colour seemed to be pouring up from a hidden fountain beyond the horizon, spreading out and upwards like a veil being pulled across the sky. As Mike watched, the colour at the source changed from pale green, through aquamarine to blue. It was breathtakingly beautiful.

Sonia spoke quietly. "I never thought I'd see that."

"How could you? I've spent all my adult life at sea. I've never seen it. Never even heard tell of it." He was still staring at the sky.

"I didn't mean the sky. It's gorgeous of course. Gorgeous."

"What did you mean then?"

"I meant you, Mike."

That brought his eyes round on to her. "I'm not in the mood for riddles."

"It's no riddle. It was you, looking at that sky. You looked like I imagine a poet looks when he gets an inspiration. You looked sort of full of wonder, awe. It was as if you'd been transported right away up there among the gods."

He stared at her. "Sonia, you shouldn't be hitting the bottle before breakfast."

"Honest, no." She shook her head. "That's how you looked, Mike. I knew you wouldn't like me saying it."

"I don't mind what you think you saw. You got it all wrong." He took her arm and led her to the rail. "Have a good look out there. The sea's full of surprises, Sonia. You get to know them when you spend your life on ships. You learn to recognise them. Even the ones you don't ever see, you hear about, or read about. When you see something like that out there, something you've never seen or heard about or read about, you don't stand and stare in wonder at the beauty of Mother Nature. You stand and stare because you're scared out of your tiny little wits."

"You don't look scared." She looked away at the painted sky. "And that doesn't scare me one little bit. It just thrills me. That's better than any sunset. That's what it is, I suppose. Some sort of trick of sun and sea."

"Maybe. More than likely you're right, Sonia. That's the trouble with all professionals. We all want the answer to be complicated. It sort of justifies our existence. "

Her eyes were wandering across the spreading curtain. "See how it's changing all the time from colour to colour. It's marvellous."

"You keep on watching. It'll probably change soon to an advert for Boozo soap or something. I'm off up to the bridge."

"Peasant," she called after him.

Stock grinned briefly as he hurried up the ladders to the bridge. He was not grinning when he arrived. He had learned to trust his instinct. It told him that that sky was a bad omen. "What d'you make of that lot?" he barked as he walked on to the bridgefront.

The senior watchkeeper was at the command console. "That sky, you mean?"

"What else?"

The officer shrugged. "I don't know what to make of it. It's quite a display."

"Is that all you've got to say?"

The watchkeeper looked nonplussed. The staff captain was in a foul mood about something.

"Well, I'll tell you something to say," snapped Stock. "Say 'sir' for a start. Then get your arse off that seat and have a look at the chart. I want to know what that's all about out there."

"Yes, sir." Good lord, his new girl friend must've slapped his face or something.

"You too, lad." This to the junior down on the bridgefront beside him.

"Yes, sir." The young officer scurried up the steps to the chart-table behind the console.

Mike took a pair of binoculars and trained them round on the bow. There was nothing but the ever changing colour. Down on the horizon at what seemed to be the source it was now a brilliant violet. "Seen the Old Man?"

"He was up here at seven. Just his usual five or ten minutes, sir."

Stock lifted the phone and buzzed for the commodore. "Stock here, sir. Could you come up top for a minute? No, nothing wrong. Not really. There's an odd looking sky down to the south. I think you should see it. Right, sir." He hooked up the phone. "Found anything?"

"There's something here, sir. But if our navigation's right, it's a devil of a long way off."

Mike stepped up to the console deck. "Let me see." He peered at the chart. It was a very small scale ocean chart. He took the magnifier and focused it. "Phoenix Island. Quite new. It's been added. Couldn't just have discovered it. Not there. A new island, eh. Up out of the sea. That makes sense. A volcano." He spanned the distance and measured it off.

"Better than a hundred miles. Nearer one fifty." He swung the glass round to the bottom of the chart. "There, lad. There's the number. Get that notice out. I want to know more about this Phoenix." He walked away from the table, beckoning the watchkeeper to follow. "You'd better sit down at the controls again." He leaned over and dropped his voice as the officer sat down. "I'm surprised at you. You shouldn't have been caught out like that. I prescribe a little less bridge in the evenings with the Norths and the commodore. You're good enough to get your promotion the usual way."

"Yes—sir." God save me from the Stocks of this world. All heave-ho-and-a-bottle-of-rum-lads one minute, then wham, right in the guts. I suppose I deserved it. That's the trouble with Stock. He's always right.

Lang was out in the starboard wing when Stock came down to the bridgefront. "Good morning, Captain Stock. Glad you called me. I wouldn't have missed this for anything."

"I could do without it, Commodore."

"Why, man? It's magnificent."

"So I'm told."

"The trouble with you, Captain, is there's no poetry in your soul. Your computers can't do anything like that."

"Thank goodness. And I've already heard about the poetry."

"Have you indeed." Lang looked round at Stock. "Any idea what it is?"

"I've an idea. We'll know in a minute."

The junior was there beside him. "Here it is, sir."

"Thanks, lad. That's all." Mike took the booklet and read the notice. He nodded and handed it to Lang. "That'll be it. Phoenix Island. It's fairly new. Came up out of the sea. It says there it still erupts now and again."

The commodore read the entry and looked back at the sky.

"I suppose it could be that."

"Have you got any other ideas?"

"No." He shook his head. "How far off are we?"

"Close on a hundred and fifty miles."

"As far as that," Lang crinkled his brows in thought. "But what can be causing all the colours?"

"I don't know. I'm not a volcano expert. Whatever's belching up out of the crater I suppose. It could be refracting the light, breaking it up like a rainbow in a shower."

"That's an idea. We had better take notes and report all this to the weather people."

"I'll fix that, sir. I'll ask Sparks to shop around for anyone else in the area. It might be interesting to know what they're seeing."

"Good idea."

Stock stared at the sky again. The violet was now almost black and the colours were darkening everywhere. The veil was spreading fast. It was already a quarter of the way from the horizon to the zenith and almost the whole way round from east to south. He said no more but he felt anxious, almost panicky, like animals feel when the sun is eclipsed. He felt sure that was what was going to happen. That spreading cloud was going to go on darkening and spreading till it shut out the sun and cocooned the ship in a daytime blackness. He wondered what it was up there in the sky. He wondered if it would stay up there. He wondered how long it would last. He smiled grimly to himself. What's the matter with you, Mike? Have you got a thing about the dark or something? No, I quite like it if the company's right. There you go again. Always ready to make with the earthy comment. The trick cyclists would find you interesting. They find everyone interesting. We're all nuts; except them, of course. They could explain all about why you dread that spreading cloud, Mike. Sure, sure. They'd say it was because my parents shut me up in a closet, or wouldn't let me have a nightlight, or belted me for peeing the bed. They'd be wrong.

It's not complicated or deep and sunk way down in my sub-
conscious. It's just that that lot up there's not normal. It's not
it that worries me. It's what it might mean.

The psychiatrists would have been wrong if they had made
that diagnosis. Mike Stock was not one of the up-by-his-own-
bootstraps brigade that people took him for. He did nothing
to encourage or deny it. His manners and attitudes were his
own, they suited him. If people thought he had risen from a
cloth cap background, that was their affair. Why disappoint
them? There were advantages in leaving things be. The
politicians were doing all right kidding people they all crawled
out of the slums.

Mike's father was a doctor. He was now in his middle
sixties. Mike's older brother was the other partner. They had
a prosperous general practice in a small market town. It was
an ideal partnership. Old Dr. Stock was strong on bedside
manner, his son looked after the serious medicine. All the
Stocks, Dr. and Mrs., senior and junior, pretended that Mike
did not exist. It would have been bad for public confidence.
But it galled them to know that the prodigal son was earning
more than he would have been following the family tradition
of medicine.

As a child, Mike had everything. He had everything except
the adventure and excitement he craved. Life was organised
to save him from all that. Life in the doctor's house was well
ordered; the house and the children had to reflect the solid
respectability that was a part of the doctor's professional status.
What he could not have, Mike soon found for himself. From
chasing the hens and setting the dog on the postman, he
graduated to scrumping apples from the rectory orchard,
scrawling on walls, plugging the coin return on phone boxes
to increase his pocket money, and damming the squire's stream
to make snaring the trout easier. It was all fairly innocent but
everyone was relieved when he went away to prep school.

Everyone but the staff at the prep school. The young Stock's ingenuity knew no bounds. He always thought his best prank was the business of the headmaster's black-out screens. That was one he never owned up to. And nobody really suspected him. It was not possible that anything so diabolical could have been thought up by a nine-year-old.

The screens had been made by the local carpenter. They were lying in the shed waiting to be taken into the house. Everyone took the blackout very seriously even out in the country during the war. All Mike did was to pierce out a pattern in tiny holes on the black cloth. The patrolling air-raid warden was stupefied when he saw a huge swastika etched across the headmaster's window. There are still those in these parts who have doubts about the headmaster's loyalty.

Mike got into public school on the strength of his family's connection with the place. His brother was a model pupil. Mike's prep school results were barely average except for maths for which he had a remarkable talent. His housemaster was a mathematician. Mike enjoyed school. He enjoyed adolescence. He got into a lot of trouble but it was all good clean fun. Nothing that lines or the cane could not put right. But then came the business of the housemaster's daughter. That was different. His father was allowed to take him away before he was expelled.

Jobs were discussed. Outdoor jobs for the two years till his National Service would take him into the forces. Mike was appalled at that prospect. He decided to try the sea. He got a cadetship with a small tanker company. It was a tramp outfit but he liked the life. By the time he had his first certificate the company had been bought over by Inoco and Mike was in at the beginning of the build-up of the British fleet.

His occasional visits home might have gone on for ever. The suddenness of his marriage severed the last links. His family might have survived it all; she was a very nice girl from a respectable background and the suspected pregnancy did not develop. But Mike would talk about it. "Shotgun affair, you know. Her old man said, 'Look here, young feller-me-lad, you tie the knot or else.' What could I do? I hate violence." Then he would laugh. His people did not think it was a laughing matter.

That sky, ever darkening, ever spreading, was not a laughing matter for Mike Stock. He knew his instinct of impending danger was probably wrong. It would turn out to be no worse than a thick Atlantic overcast. But he was not his usual self as he munched his breakfast. Gene North wanted to know all about the sky and Phoenix Island. There was little to tell. Sonia had seen the colours deepening into violet and black. In itself it meant nothing to her but she could see that Mike was uneasy. Some of his unease rubbed off on her.

By half past ten that morning the cloud had overtaken the sun. The cloud was black, jet black, except at its leading edge where bands of colour rippled and blended, merged back into the blackness, then reappeared ahead of it. They seemed out of place, like pageant banners fluttering on a hearse. As the cloud reached the sun the coloured bands fairly jigged with delight. They seemed to touch the sun, then surround it, push it back and forward, tease it. Then they shackled it and drove it back into the cloud. The sun was silver, then green, blue, violet. Then it was gone behind the black screen and half the sea was suddenly in deep twilight.

From the bridge of the *Emperor* they watched the progress of the black veil. The commodore was there, Stock was there, the Norths were there. They watched, then looked away, talked about it, reassured each other; but always their eyes were drawn back up to the uncanny sky. Looking away from it, now that the sun was covered, the spreading twilight reminded them of it. That was the only thing that was not normal. The

166

sea was there, calm, almost glass smooth on top of the heaving swell. The noise of the water displaced by the huge bow was still there, gurgling, splashing, racing along the sides to join the white wake astern. There was no real wind but the ship's own wind poured in a constant refreshing stream through ports and doors. There was the feel of the distant engines and the small sounds of the automatic controls keeping the ship on course.

The Sparks had trouble raising any response to his calls. It was a bad time of day for short wave work. Medium wave transmission to the south, towards Midway, was being snarled and distorted by the cloud. There seemed to be no ships for hundreds of miles in any direction. That was to be expected. The *Emperor* was well south of the usual trans-Pacific tracks. When he did get through to Midway, the message said nothing they had not already guessed. But it was reassuring. There was nothing to worry about. Phoenix Island was in eruption. More spectacularly than usual. The cloud was ash thrown up from the crater. It was travelling north and spreading out east and west on an upper level wind from the south. Aircraft were keeping the island under observation.

"Congratulations, Captain," said Lang. "You were right."

"It didn't take a genius to work that out. We don't know any more than we knew before. I suppose it's nice to know they think there's nothing to worry about."

"There isn't, is there?"

"I don't know. I just don't like it."

"It is a bit spooky," said Sonia. "But I suppose we should be pleased. We must be almost the only people in the whole world to be seeing this."

Stock gave her a small smile. "That's true."

"Very remarkable," announced Gene. "I must say the whole thing's absolutely fascinating."

"The show's not over yet," Mike told him. "Look down

167

there to the south. That horizon's shortening all the time. That muck up there's starting to drop."

They all looked. It was true. The blackness now seemed to be rearing up out of the sea only a few miles from the ship.

"What've you got on radar?" called Stock.

"No targets, sir. Clutter all down the starboard side about eight miles and closing."

"What'd I tell you." He spoke to the watchkeeper again. "Let's see the remote display."

"Coming up, sir."

The repeater screen down on the bridgefront flickered and lit up. "There you are," said Mike. "That stippled segment there. That's whatever it is, ash or dust. Solid enough to throw back an echo anyway."

"Absolutely fascinating," said Gene again. He was genuinely interested. His eyes moved from the radar screen out through the door to the black sky and the sea.

Sonia watched too. She was now a little apprehensive with the sun shut out and the dropping debris of the volcano marching across the water towards the ship. She slipped an arm through Gene's and gripped his wrist.

"Can I give out a few instructions, sir?" asked Mike.

Lang nodded. "Carry on, Captain. You know what's needed. You don't need me to tell you."

"Yes, sir." Silly old crow. Of course I don't need you to tell me. I don't need you, period. Sometimes I wonder if you're getting delusions of grandeur. You're really laying on the big commodore stuff pretty thick. Look at you now. Standing there like the hero in a soap opera, smirking away as if you knew it all. You should have a big placard on your chest saying "Nothing scares me." We'll see. I've spent a long time cocking a snook at just about everything. But never Mother Nature. No, sir.

Mike went up to the control deck and sat down in one of the

spare chairs. He pulled over a handset and stabbed a button. "Chief? Hallo, George. That cloud's going to come down on us soon. I'm just going to get the whole ship closed up tight so we'll want full air conditioning from now on." He listened. "So you'll have problems. So you'll solve them. You're the technical wizard. Just think of my lovely paintwork." He listened then grinned. "O.K. By the way, try and squeeze another knot or so out of her. The sooner we're through this lot, the better." He pressed another button. "Chef, send enough food for the rest of the day along midships. It's going to start raining cinders. We don't want to get like stokers with that long walk aft." He pushed away the handset and switched on the public address. "Now hear this, hear this. Captain Stock here. Close all ports and doors, repeat, all ports and doors. We're going to run through a cloud of muck. Hear this, off duty watches. Hear this, off duty watches. Report to operations room. Operations room. Out."

The whole crew had been briefed by noon when the first flakes of ash floated down on to the ship. The sky to the north was still lit by the hidden sun, but palely, and the ship steamed through a deep premature twilight. The running lights were on and the ash could be seen in their glow. The flakes were random at first but soon they came in droves, dropping almost straight through the windless air but seeming to sweep in like driven snow as the *Emperor* plunged ahead at full speed.

Everyone watched for a few seconds in silence. Sonia was the first to speak. "It's like snow."

"But black," said Mike.

"Yes, but you can't tell. Not up there in the lights. Just because it doesn't show white when it lands."

"I suppose that's right." Stock laughed. "It's funny, you know. I didn't like that cloud one little bit when it was up there. Now it's coming down, it doesn't seem the least bit frightening."

"The evil you know and all that," said Gene.

"Maybe that's it."

It was Lang's turn. "I told you there was nothing to fear in a spot of volcanic ash."

"It wasn't the ash that worried me," replied Mike sourly. "It was what it might mean."

"What could it mean?"

"If I knew, I wouldn't have been worried."

"But you're not worried now."

"No. I can't think why but, as Sonia says, it's just like black snow."

"Isn't there somewhere that gets black snow?" asked Sonia.

Everyone agreed there was. No one could remember where.

It was only minutes before the first sulphurous scent came through the ventilation system. That was a surprise. It was not overpowering but it was unpleasant. It destroyed the illusion of separateness from the ash-laden world outside.

The commodore seemed oblivious to the renewed depression. He took the Norths down to lunch and entertained them with stories of the sea and ships. It was quite a gay luncheon party. The atmosphere in the midships dining room was so different from up on the bridge. The curtains were drawn and all the lights were on. The steward on duty had sprayed the room with one of those fragrant disinfectants to destroy the smell from outside. He was the kind of steward who would get on.

After lunch, Lang announced that he was going to check up on what was happening on the bridge then have his usual siesta. Sonia and Gene went to their own quarters. They thought they would not sleep. But the steward had sprayed their rooms too. There was no sign there of the black ash outside. They were both soon asleep.

Stock stayed up on the bridge. By three in the afternoon the cloud had shut out the whole sky and it was dark like a winter midnight. The ash and dust poured down on the ship. On the tank decks the sprinklers trapped the muck, turned it to mud, rolled it to the scuppers to gush in filthy streams over the side. Every hour, half a dozen men would come out on deck, robot-like, awkward in the big smoke helmets to hose away the ash piling up on running lights, radar scanners, radio aerials. Elsewhere, it landed, flurried, drifted, built up. The air intakes for the air conditioning soon clogged. The engineers blew them clear again. Then they rigged spray nozzles to throw a water curtain across the intakes. That worked well. It even seemed to lessen the smell inside the ship. The ash lay thick on the water, turning the ocean into a vast field of slurry. The ship ploughed through it, splitting the black blanket, carving out a wide gash of green and white. On board, every sound seemed louder than before. Sounds were heard, traced and identified; sounds no one had ever noticed. Normal sounds but now heard for the first time as the insulating cloud of ash bounced them back on the ears.

Mike paced the bridgefront. He sat up at the console. There was nothing he could do but check on what was already being done. But he stayed up there. He stayed there all afternoon, then all through the night. He stayed as the watches changed there and down in the operations room and out on deck. He stayed because there was nothing he could do. Nothing would stop till they got clear of that suffocating pall of cinder and dust. He munched sandwiches, he drank coffee. He smoked a bit but stopped when his throat went dry. The air filters were not stopping everything. Fine soft black dust was settling in every space inside the ship, hanging unseen in the smelly air. He catnapped at the console with his feet up on one of the spare chairs. Every time he woke, he peered at the time, he peered outside. The interminable black blizzard was always there. Sparks could raise no one on the radio. The *Emperor* was alone, cut off from the rest of the world.

171

Near midnight there was a change. There was a lightness in the sky. Spirits rose. Prematurely. The black rain had stopped. It was now a fine white pumice dust. Stock told the watch to take a sample to add to the ones they already had. The change of type and colour in the cloud meant nothing to him. It was welcome in that it dispelled the terrible blackness, though only slightly as it came in the night. That white dust would have meant much more to a vulcanologist.

In the early hours of the morning the Sparks picked up a message from the aircraft patrolling near Phoenix Island. It was freak reception in the conditions but it was very welcome. Phoenix Island had stopped erupting. The white dust still dropped from the sky but now it was only a matter of time till the cloud moved clear to the north. The *Emperor* steamed on eastwards.

The Norths had spent the evening with the commodore. They had drinks and talked. There was no fourth to play bridge. Everyone else was on duty or trying to sleep. The dust was the only real sign of what was going on outside. They noticed it as it smeared their fingers and faces and clothes. Sonia thought she felt it in her hair and in her eyes. But it seemed nothing at all when she peered out of a port and saw the swirling cloud. They all turned in early. Sonia put her arms round her husband in bed and held him tight. "It's been a funny sort of day, darling."

"Yes, it has, hasn't it. Tomorrow will be all right though. This can't last."

"Oh, the dirt hasn't been so bad, Gene. We've been lucky. We've hardly noticed it. I just kept getting that spooky feeling when I looked out and saw the whole world raining blackness."

"Hmm. I know what you mean."

"Do you, darling? I wonder if you do. You and the commodore were the only ones who didn't seem to feel that way. Isn't he marvellous? You'd think he went through this kind of thing every day of life. He's really at home at sea, isn't he. He's like the old sailors they write about."

"Yes, I think he is." He reached out and switched off the light. Yes, I think he is. Gene had said as much in his journal only minutes before. He had reminded himself that he had wanted to see Stock and Lang together in an emergency. Now he had seen it and he had been right about whom to put his money on. Not that Captain Stock was anything but efficient. It was just that Lang had that overall control of the situation; calm, unflappable, supremely confident. It was a pity he was retiring soon. His was a dying breed.

CHAPTER FIFTEEN

Phoenix Island disappeared four minutes after nine o'clock the next morning. It did not disappear as other new islands often do. It did not slide back under the sea leaving a column of smoke and steam for minutes or hours to mark where it had been. Phoenix Island disappeared in the biggest explosion ever recorded. "Cataclysmic" was the soberest description used by copywriters throughout the world. Their less inhibited colleagues piled adjective upon adjective, comparison upon comparison, in frantic attempts to describe adequately the indescribable.

Much later, when the scientists had had time to study the evidence, theories were announced. They were not unanimous except about the basic facts. The pressure wave from Phoenix circled the earth ten times. The explosion was heard at distances of almost four thousand miles. It was heard in Los

Angeles and San Francisco and Vancouver. It was heard in Tokyo, Shanghai, Manila and Darwin. The energy released was equivalent to the detonation of between one and two million hydrogen bombs. Seismographs jerked and quivered and recorded the unbelievable. The pulverised debris shot straight up in the classic pine tree shape. At the top of the trunk, at five miles high, then on up to more than twenty miles above the sea, the mushroom shape of the foliage blossomed. That cloud was to circle the earth for years. It was to reduce the sun's radiation by more than ten per cent and give the world the most spectacular sunrises and sunsets of all time. It was to affect the weather in the northern hemisphere. The scientists could never agree about this but the facts were there. The winters of '69, '70, and '71 in America and Europe were to be colder and longer than since records had been kept. Summers were cool. Areas of high rainfall suffered drought. Deserts became quagmires. In Washington and London, Paris and Moscow that cloud meant something worse than cold air and drought and flood. It meant that satellite communication systems were scrambled, missile trajectories threatened, space shots jeopardised. It meant crash programmes of satellite launchings and new calculations.

The waves were the least noticed effect of the Phoenix cataclysm. They ran out across the ocean like the ripples from a stone dropped in a fish pond. But the stone had been mountain sized, not dropped but exploded. The leading wave topped three hundred feet in height as it started its journey. It was less a wave than a precipice of water. Days later on the other side of the world the water level in the English Channel rose several inches. Before that the waves had struck elsewhere. In California they arrived on the back of the Pacific swell as huge breakers. They ran up beaches, destroyed houses, spilled over on to highways. But they were expected. Even the beach bums had been evacuated. To the north and south the waves ran out across the line of the swell, losing their size and power, but still hitting the Aleutians and the mid-Pacific islands ferociously. To the west, they surged into the teeth of the ocean swell and were harnessed and slowed and stopped before they reached Japan and the mainland of Asia.

What happened at Phoenix Island had happened before. But it had never happened before in that depth of water or on that fantastic scale. For twenty hours, from daylight the day before, the volcano had been erupting furiously. The magma, the molten rocks and gases which boiled up from deep under the sea, had blasted out the plugs it had formed during its last eruption and exploded from the crater cone in an avalanche of red hot debris. The pressure behind it had thrown it high to form the spreading cloud of cinders and ash and dust which had dropped over the *Emperor*. The eruption was so violent that it had quickly exhausted the magma, leaving a vast cavern inside the mountain. Phoenix Island was a mountain. True it only showed a hundred feet or so above the sea. That was just the peak. It stretched down six thousand feet to the sea bed. New magma poured up from deep in the earth. When the cavern was filled again, there would be another eruption. There never was. The hollowed mountain could not for long support its own weight. That morning, a third of it collapsed into itself. Millions of gallons of water poured into the cavern. The magma had liquefied the mountain debris in an instant; now it met and vaporised the water. The steam had a thousand times more volume than the water it had come from. The steam and the rising magma with all its debris and gases exploded inside the truncated mountain with unimaginable ferocity. The whole mountain was demolished, its sides pulverised by the blast. The magma roared upwards in a vertical column of liquid rock and steam and gas. That was the trunk of the pine tree that was to become its own mushroom cloud. It was the outward blast under the sea, the blast that demolished the mountain, that made the waves. And it was the waves that were to threaten the world's biggest ship.

At four minutes past nine that morning the *Emperor* was three hundred and fifty miles east north east of Phoenix Island. She had logged a full seventeen knots through the night with the swell helping her along. No one on board heard the great explosion. It vaulted high for five hundred miles in every direction. The first news they got was from intercepted messages from the aircraft patrolling south of the island.

No one on that aircraft saw the actual explosion. The co-pilot almost did. He was staring out of his side window down and across at the island. It was quiet down there. The eruption had stopped hours before. The light was tricky, fairly bright where they were, deeply shaded over and north of the island where the sun was still struggling with the thinning ash cloud. Afterwards, he remembered thinking he saw the whole island disappear into a hole in the sea which immediately became a whirlpool. He shook his head and closed his eyes tight. He promised himself to give up these long beer and poker sessions like last night's. He opened his eyes. Wide. His mouth opened to speak to the pilot. The words never came. The aircraft was flung across the sky like a scrap of paper caught in a hurricane. For seconds it seemed impossible that the pilot could regain control. The plane rolled over and over as if launched on a mad display of aerobatics. Both pilots were only held in their seats by their lap straps. Other crew members rolled about inside the fuselage, shocked, winded, desperately grabbing for handholds. But the pilot did regain control. He got control as the plane dived. He eased her up slowly till she was flying flat and level. Then he called his crew.

"You guys all right back there? Come on, come on. Hurry it up. Report in."

They checked in one by one. Nobody more than bruised.

He looked round at the co-pilot. "Now what the hell was that all about?"

The other man was still trying to catch his breath. "The island, Skip. It—it disappeared. Like—like down a hole or something."

"Where the hell is it anyway?" They both peered around trying to orientate themselves.

"Gee-zus."

"My Gawd."

They watched as the plane came round to give them a clear sight. The intercom chattered as the rest of the crew saw it.

"All right, all right. Shut up and let me look."

They all looked, spellbound. The huge column of black and red and green and blue stood up into the sky like a painted tree. As they watched, the top bellied out as it rose, to form that ominous shape.

"Gawd, it's like the bomb. On a long stalk."

The co-pilot whistled. "We're lucky to come out of that lot in one piece."

"You can say that again." The pilot stretched forward and peered down. "D'you say that island seemed to disappear?"

"That's what it looked like, Skip. It was there, then it wasn't there. It looked like the water was all swirled up where it had been. Then boomph."

"We'd better radio the base." He spoke into his microphone. "Sparks, take this message for Midway. 'Urgent. Phoenix Island exploded. Column of debris already twenty thousand feet, rising and mushrooming.'" He listened as the radio man read it back to him. Then he spoke to one of the others. "Will you shut up, Minski? I'm trying to think."

"Sorry, skipper, but it's these ripples down there. You see them?"

"Ripples?"

"Yeah, like when you throw a brick in a puddle."

The pilot dropped the nose and looked. "I see them. Thanks, Minski." He turned to the co-pilot. "Some ripples. They must be mighty big to show like that from up here."

"Well, let's be glad we're up here. Any ship down there's in for a rough ride."

"Christ, ships. I forgot about that." He pushed the nose farther down into a steep dive. "Sparks, add to that message. 'Large waves observed radiating from explosion centre. Investigating.'" The plane roared downwards to the east aiming to meet the leading wave. "How long since the big bang?"

The co-pilot checked his watch. "Five, ten minutes. No more."

"Say ten minutes. And that wave down there's twenty-five, thirty miles out already. That's the best part of two hundred knots."

"Can waves go that fast, Skip?"

"How do I know? But that one is." He pulled the nose up. The wave was running ahead of his aiming point. "At least."

At a thousand feet he flattened the aircraft out and flew across the first wave. He flew on while the crew looked back and oohed and aahed at its size. He banked and turned and dropped the plane nearer the sea. "Watch it now."

The co-pilot read the altimeter. "500. 400. 350. 300. That's about it, Skip. Three hundred feet. Gee—zus." They watched as the plane and the wave raced towards each other. "Up, Skip, up." The voice was urgent.

The plane angled sharply and zoomed over the crest, its belly clear only by feet.

The pilot blew hard from his mouth and shook his head. "Real fast. Gawd. I nearly put her right in." He wiped the back of his hand across his face, holding the aircraft up to gain height again. "Sparks, CQ to all ships. 'Tidal waves three hundred feet high running all directions from Phoenix Island estimated speed two hundred knots.' Then send it to Midway and tell them we'll patrol the east side. They better send someone west."

When the Sparks on the *Emperor* intercepted the plane's first message to Midway, Captain Stock was standing at the after end of the lower bridge desk with Sonia. He had given up his night long vigil on the bridge two hours before when the commodore came up for his morning look round.

Lang had been in an immense good humour. He said a cheerful "good morning" then walked from wing to wing across the bridge, looking fore and aft. When he stopped amidships Stock had come down from the console deck. "Well, Captain, it seems that your premonitions were unfounded after all."

"Yes, sir." Mike was too tired to argue. And it did seem that he had worried himself unnecessarily. The ash cloud was still there but it was thin and white with pumice. The swell was there, running ahead past the bridge, the water clear now of the black filth of yesterday. Hardly any ash was falling, just an occasional flake, white, like small snow. Here and there on the water long streaks of soapy looking pumice stretched across the swell like effluent on a running river. Mike was tired, his eyes red rimmed with dust and lack of sleep, his uniform rumpled and streaked with black dust. Beside Lang, fresh from the tub, fragrant with talc and after shave, and dressed in clean crisp linen, he felt like the coalman calling at the front door.

"Jolly good to see the sun again," announced the commodore.

Stock looked. Yes, I suppose it's nice. The sun was there in the north east, low still, but recognisable. The pumice cloud showed it as a dull silver circle like a coin suspended above the horizon. The light all around had that same silvery tone, unnatural, eerie, as if contrived for some special effect in a theatre.

179

"Come on now, Captain Stock. Cheer up, man. We all make mistakes. All of us. You were right to look on the black side. Always best to expect the worst. Anyway it hasn't happened, has it. You run along now and have a hot shower and a bite to eat. You'll be a new man."

"Yes, sir," was all Mike risked.

Lang had been right about the shower and breakfast. It helped. But Mike still felt jaded, uneasy, as he went out to see how the cleaning up was going. The high pressure hoses were making short work of the muck that had accumulated off the main decks. He could not turn on his bright and breezy self for Sonia.

"Hello, Mike," she said quietly.

"Hallo there. How're you?"

"Well, thank you. I'm ashamed to say I slept like a baby."

"Good for you."

"Did you get some sleep?"

"A bit. Not much."

"I'm sorry." She brightened. "But you can catch up on it today. All that filthy black stuff's gone. I was covered with dust this morning but it all washed off and I feel fine now."

"Good."

"Mike, what's the matter with you? All right so you were up half the night. All right so you were wrong about something awful happening. So what? Did you want something awful to happen?"

"Don't be so damned silly." He turned away and called down to one of the men on deck.

Sonia glared at his back. I knew it. I knew it as soon as I woke up this morning. Maybe before I went to sleep last night. I've gone off you, Captain Michael Stock. All gay and jolly when it suits your book then as sour as a lemon as soon as things don't go your way. You're just like a little boy who's had his toys taken away. That's it, just like a little boy. It's the same with your women and your flirting. Adolescent, that's what it is. God, when will I ever learn. It's always happening to me. I never take time. I like people on sight, I expect them to be normal and simple like me. Then bang, right on the jaw. They turn out to be worms or worse.

The public address bellowed above her head. "Captain Stock to the bridge. Captain Stock to the bridge."

Mike went up the ladder like a scalded cat. Sonia watched him go, up and round the walkway to the wing of the bridge and inside. What now? Dear God, straighten this thing out for me. Now I suspect maybe I'm wrong again, and all just because he's called to the bridge. What the devil am I worried about anyway? I'm not married to him. I just thought I liked him. No, I suppose it's because I know he's bright. If he's worried about something, that should mean something. It all seems to be over, that ash and mess. Could there still be something? She shrugged and went inside.

The watchkeeper called out as soon as Stock came on to the bridgefront. "Sparks has picked up something, sir. Phoenix Island's just exploded."

Mike stopped. In that second, all his tiredness drained away. He was relieved and worried at one and the same time. His premonition had been right. But did it mean anything to the ship? "Anything else?"

"Nothing much. 'Column of debris already twenty thousand feet rising and mushrooming.' "

"Anything showing on your instruments?"

"Nothing here."

"How far off are we?"

"Wait a minute, sir."

Stock took a few steps across the bridgefront.

"We're better than three hundred and fifty miles off now. Thank goodness too. That'll be why we heard nothing."

"There may be time yet. Sound is funny stuff. Takes time.

Easily deflected. That must've been some bang." He walked back to the starboard door. "Tell Sparks to keep listening."

"He's doing that. Says reception's pretty dicey."

"All the more reason to listen like a hawk."

"Yes, sir." Then almost at once, "Something else, sir. Something about big waves, Sparks says. He didn't get it all."

Mike nodded and looked out at the gently heaving sea. Waves. Yes, that was predictable. Maybe wind and more ash too. But the distance will save us from all that. "What's the bearing of that island now?" He waited.

"It should be almost exactly two points on the starboard quarter, sir. Should have been, rather."

Mike nodded. He stepped through the door into the wing of the bridge and looked aft on that bearing. Nothing. What'd you expect, you silly fool? Three fifty's a long way even to see a mushroom cloud. And that white ash is still up there in the way. Better tell old Lang. Dammit, no. Wait. See what happens. Soon enough to call him when I know something.

Twenty minutes past nine.

"Captain Stock, sir."

"Yes." He stepped back inside.

"Here's a CQ, sir. I think the figures are a bit garbled. It couldn't be."

"Just read it," barked Stock.

"Yes, sir. 'Tidal waves three hundred feet high running all directions from Phoenix Island estimated speed two hundred knots.' You see what I mean, sir? Something wrong somewhere."

Mike's stomach felt like a balled fist. Tidal waves. Extreme stress. "What does Sparks say? Is that exactly what he got?"

"That's what was sent. So he says."

"Write it down. Write it down on a message pad." Mike grabbed the phone and buzzed the commodore. "Stock here.

You'd better come up top." He slammed the phone back on its hook and stepped back into the wing and stared aft.

The commodore came up the inside stair. "What is it this time, Captain?" He sounded tolerant.

Mike took the message form from the quartermaster and passed it to Lang without a word.

The commodore read it. He read it again. "What is all this nonsense, Captain? Waves three hundred feet high. Travelling at two hundred knots."

"Oh, of course, you haven't heard. Phoenix Island blew itself to bits about half an hour ago. That's what caused the waves."

"Blew itself to bits? Why wasn't I told? When was this?"

"I just told you. About half an hour ago. I didn't say anything at first. I wanted to be sure this time."

"Captain Stock, you know perfectly well I should be informed immediately of anything like this. But as for being sure; is this it?" He waved the message in the air. "Is this your being sure? This lot of misread claptrap?"

Stock was not even looking at the commodore. He was gazing aft. "All that Sparks guaranteed is that that claptrap is what was sent."

"By whom, may I ask?"

"It says U.S. Air Force on that form."

"Hmm. So it does." Lang shook his head and smiled. "That's certainly what it says but you must agree the figures are ridiculous. Have you ever heard of a three hundred foot high wave? Probably three hundred feet long. Or thirty feet high. And as for that speed. Two hundred knots. Pah. Twenty."

"My turn now. Tell me, Commodore. Have you ever heard of an island poking up out from the sea where it's six or seven thousand feet deep—wait for it—have you ever heard of one like that blowing itself to bits, boom, like that?"

"No, can't say I have. Seems very unlikely. I suppose that

came from the same source as this. Too much booze last night probably. Or maybe just a silly hoax."

The pressure wave answered the speculation. It hurled Stock back against the fore end of the bridge wing. Lang staggered. They both shook their heads to and fro.

"What the devil was that?" demanded Lang.

Mike was pinching his nose and blowing. "Pressure, I suppose. Think it was all a hoax now? That blast travelled three hundred and fifty miles in about half an hour."

"I'll accept that, fantastic though it seems. I'll accept there's a wave or waves. There would be, wouldn't there. But not three hundred feet and two hundred knots."

"All right, Commodore." Mike turned to face him. "We'll agree to differ on the size and speed. But there is a wave. More like several. Can we agree to take a few elementary precautions?"

"We'll do that, naturally. The usual extreme weather precautions."

"Thank you, Commodore. Can I suggest a bit more? One, that we increase speed even at the risk of shaking some of the chief's nuts and bolts loose. Two, that we sort out the ballast to give us a chance of not breaking in two if that wave does reach us."

"I don't suppose that can do any harm. But you're being pessimistic as usual, Captain. We're in very deep water here. And that wave's a long way off. Distance and depth will soon cut it down to size."

"I hope you're right, sir. I'm not pessimistic. I'm just concerned for fifteen million pounds' worth of ship and thirty-five men. And don't forget our big man from New York and his wife."

Lang sniffed and began pacing up and down across the bridgefront.

Stock spoke first to the chief engineer. He thought he might coax another half knot out of the engines. The staff captain thanked him and rang off. A mile, a mile and a half. It was a gesture only but you could never tell. Next, he called a watch to the operations room and gave instructions about switching the ballast. Then he spoke into the public address.

"Now hear this, hear this. Captain Stock here. That island that showered all that muck on us yesterday has just blown itself to bits. It's made a big wave that's coming our way. We're well clear so there's nothing to worry about. We're just taking precautions. Listen carefully." He paused for a few seconds. "If this wave reaches us, and if it's still big, the commodore will turn the ship round and take it bow on. There might be a bit of a bump. We'll give you warning. But we don't want anyone flung about and hurt. So, as of now, put on your life jackets. I repeat, all hands put on your life jackets. The padding may save you a broken rib. Then, when you're warned, get quickly to an athwartships bulkhead. Sit down on the deck, facing aft, with your back to that bulkhead. If you can find a pillow or a cushion or other padding, keep it handy and lean against it. Pick your position now." He went over it all again. "Now, for those who'll be at the control consoles on the bridge, operations room, engine control, and radio room. You'll have to stay in your positions. Get padding and put it between yourselves and the desk tops when the time comes. If it comes. Then bend yourselves over the padding, head on hands. I'll go over it all again." He went over it point by point. "Right. Now it may never happen. Probably won't. But be ready. Any queries to the departmental officers on duty. One thing more. As of now, no one on deck and all doors and storm doors shut and bolted, all ports shut and deadlights in place. That's all."

Mike dropped the microphone back into its slot. He lay back in his chair, checking over details in his mind. The ballast, that's the important thing. If she hangs across a really big crest she could break her back. It all depends on that joint. He had to guess how the maximum stress might come. He was moving the water ballast into the midship tanks to sag the *Emperor* within ten per cent of the joint's limit. Then if she did straddle a big crest, there would be the biggest possible hogging effect available to let the bow and stern droop without splitting her into two parts. If, on the other hand, she sat across a deep trough between two huge waves, she would sag and there might not be enough resistance left in that joint. It could happen either way. He had to make a decision. He made it. He prayed he had chosen well. Entry will be important too. Not too much speed but enough to let her grip. Not too little speed so she broaches to and lies broadside on. God, I hope I'm imagining it all. How many tons of water could a three hundred foot wave drop on us? Even a hundred foot wave. Water. That's a thought. Must check with the chief on closing off the air intakes. Not too difficult.

He stared down from behind the console at the commodore pacing up and down. Well, I hope you got the message. I've told you what to do it if comes to that. Don't suppose you even heard me. You're parading up and down there like Captain Bligh on the quarter deck. I envy your confidence, Lang, if that's what it is.

The Norths came up the inside stairway. They were both carrying lifejackets. They looked around then Gene spoke to Lang. "Commodore, what's going on? Is all this true what we heard just now? Or is it some sort of exercise?"

"Don't worry, Mr. North. It's a bit of both really. It's true about the island. It's not at all likely there'll be an emergency."

"I see," said Gene slowly. He looked round and saw Stock up on the console deck. "You put the wind up both of us, Captain," he called.

"Sorry," said Mike. "I thought I made it clear it might never happen. Would you put on your lifejackets, please. When the time comes, if it comes, I suggest you come up here and take two of these chairs. Down in the cabins, the gear might fly about a bit."

Sonia and Gene both held up the lifejackets and peered at them.

"Quartermaster," said Stock. "Help Mr. and Mrs. North with their lifejackets. And when you've done that, go down and bring up the commodore's."

Ten o'clock. Another CQ from the aircraft. "Eastern sector wave now estimated two hundred feet plus. Speed of advance two hundred knots minus. Now approximately one seventy-five miles from Phoenix position. All ships in area report to this call sign."

Stock passed the message down to Lang. He read it and looked up. "What did I tell you, Captain? Height and speed dropping."

"Not enough though. It's half-way here already."

Lang waved his hand. "Don't worry, man. You're making mountains out of molehills." He went back to his pacing.

Stock shook his head. That's an unfortunate comparison, Lang. Let's pray you're right though.

Sonia was in the seat beside him, Gene next to her. The two watchkeepers were on his other side. Sonia whispered to him. "Mike, is it really bad? Tell me. Is it?"

He patted her hand. "It might be a bit rough. But don't worry, Mrs. Millionaire. We'll get you back in one piece to Tiffany's."

She snatched her hand away and glared at him.

Ten-thirty. The wave was reported at two hundred and fifty miles from Phoenix. The *Emperor* had run twenty-six miles since nine o'clock. One hundred plus twenty-six. A hundred and twenty-six miles astern. Estimated height one seventy/one eighty feet. Speed of advance down to one fifty.

Lang read it all. "Just what I said. Dropping all the time. That plane's estimates are high, of course."

"Why so?" asked Mike, idly, not really expecting an answer.

"Because the pilot's not a seaman, that's why. I couldn't estimate a plane's height within a hundred feet. What makes you think a pilot's guess at wave height would be any better?"

Mike said nothing, looked away. Sonia stuck her tongue out at him.

Everyone waited for the next report. Outside the sea looked normal. The sky was brighter. Reports came in from the operations room on the ballast shifting. Another half-hour to complete it. Plenty of time. The commodore walked the bridgefront like a caged lion, but calmly.

Just before eleven o'clock Sparks reported the aircraft close by and calling on the R/T.

"Put him on the bridge speaker," ordered Stock.

As the speaker came alive and the pilot's voice sounded in the bridge, they all heard the roar of the plane as it swooped in low across the ship.

CHAPTER SIXTEEN

"Hello down there. Hello down there. Come in, *Inoco Emperor*."

"Captain Stock here. How's that wave?"

"Hello, Captain. It's coming. You've got half an hour. Maybe more. But you're big enough for it."

"Glad you think so. We'd feel better up there with you." He could see the plane turning ahead of the ship.

"Don't worry. You're big enough. That fellow down to the south-west isn't. He's had it if you don't reach him in time."

"What fellow? What d'you mean, reach him?" Stock

188

peered at the radar screen. There was a small intermittent echo about twenty-five miles away on the starboard quarter.

"Fisherman. One of those long range Jap jobs. Going like a bat out of hell but he hasn't a chance."

"Too bad. We can't reach him before that wave."

"You can try, Captain."

"Be your age. There are people on board here too. D'you want us all killed?"

"I'll speak." It was the commodore. He was standing down on the bridgefront glaring up at Stock. "I'll speak, Captain."

Stock glared back but connected the bridgefront microphone.

The pilot was talking again. "You can't mean it, Captain. You can't let these men die without trying. D'you hear me?"

"This is Commodore Lang. Don't worry. We're turning now." He signalled the alteration to starboard. "Give us a bearing and distance, please."

Stock interrupted. "We've got him on the radar. But we haven't a chance."

"Hard a starboard was the order, Captain Stock." Lang turned away and spoke into the microphone. "We have him on our radar. Can you turn him this way?"

"You bet, Commodore. Right away. Thanks and the best of luck. We're low on fuel. We won't be back. Out."

Lang put down the microphone, turned and roared. "I ordered hard a starboard. Are you deaf, man?"

Stock spun the gyro controls. "Take over," he told the watchkeeper. "And warn everyone we'll be rolling about a bit." He whirled the chair and got up. He went down to the bridge-front and faced the commodore. "Hard a starboard it is, sir. And for the record, I think you must be out of your tiny mind."

"Is that so? I'll put that in the record, Captain. I'm sure the company will find it interesting."

"If they ever see it. Maybe they will. In the rest of the wreckage."

"Oh, shut up, man. With you, everything's got to be dramatised." He gripped at the window ledge as the ship came round beam on to the swell and rolled. "I'll also put in the record that you refused to go to the aid of another ship. Try and explain that. A shipmaster's first duty."

"Balls. His first duty's to his own ship and his own crew." He stretched out his hand and tapped at the commodore's uniform. "You've got too many of these medals, Lang. You want to play the hero all the time. You're over the hill. You've lost the place."

Lang clenched his fists as he strove for control. He spoke quietly, angrily. "Now listen you to me. I'm in command here. I'm taking this ship back to get these men off that boat and on board here before that wave arrives. No ifs, no buts. You can do what the hell you want. Just don't try and interfere."

Stock shook his head. "O.K. I'm here so I might as well go back up on to that console." He turned away then half turned back. "What is it with you, Commodore? Is it because they're Japs?"

Lang whirled away and stared ahead through the window. His whole body was tensed. His hands gripped the ledge. He had made his decision on impulse. Now he wondered if Stock had fingered his real motive. Had he turned back, risking his ship and crew, as a salve to his conscience? Was he trying to save these fishermen as a penance for Yashawa's death?

Gene North watched it all from his seat on the console deck. His face showed nothing of what was going through his mind. He only heard snatches of what was said but he did not need to hear anything. The way the two men faced each other explained it all. Lang had won. That satisfied him. Mature, that was the word for the commodore. Quiet, almost unobtrusive, but ready when the time came to show his teeth. More than a match for Stock. God, how could Stock sit there and refuse to try and save these men from certain death? Lang didn't hesitate for a minute. He knew his duty, knew the risks, weighed them, made a decision. That's exercising command. Making decisions, brave decisions, the right decisions.

Gene braced his feet on the deck to stop his chair swinging as the ship rolled. Stock's got qualities too though. He said his piece and lost. Now he's back up here in his chair carrying on as if nothing had happened. No, that's not true. He's carrying on but he's watching Lang like a cat watching a mouse. Why? Certainly we'll meet this wave earlier than we would have done. But not much. The wave will be higher and faster because of that but can the difference be significant? Surely not. A foot or two. A knot or two. That can't make much difference. Surely. He gave Sonia a small smile and nodded at her encouragingly. She's a brave girl. She must be scared out of her wits but she's got control of herself. He smiled at her again.

Mike Stock was carrying on. There was a lot to do. He spoke to the chief engineer first. "George, we're now on an errand of mercy. Try and squeeze some more out of these nuts and bolts of yours."

"What d'you think I've got back here, Mike? Every time you call, you want more speed."

"Do your best. I'll call you a few minutes before that wave hits us. Get her down then to manoeuvring speed and pray. I'll keep her on bridge control but you sit by ready to take over back aft if I lose it."

"Right you are. You make it sound nasty."

"Could be."

Next he called the operations room and gave instructions to make ready grab nets, messenger ropes, an inflatable dinghy on each side. "Get them ready, then get back up off the decks."

191

The duty officer reported all the ballast shifted. Stock acknowledged and prayed he had judged that right.

The *Emperor* was corkscrewing, plunging across the swell at an angle, throwing spray across her deck and up against the bridge windows. It was as if the weather had changed but it was just the same. Hardly any wind even. Stock had been expecting gale force winds, the explosion action like the centre of a tropical storm. None came.

The watchkeeper pointed at the radar screen. "He's drawing to starboard, sir."

"He's got the wrong course, the silly bastard." Stock called Sparks. "Get that Jap on the R/T." To the watchkeeper. "Track him. Give me an interception course." To Sparks. "Put him on the bridge speaker." Mike spun the rudder control to bring the ship ahead of the fishing boat. Frantic foreign voices jabbered. "Shut up and listen, will you. Steer o—5—o. D'you get that? o—5—o. Fifty. For Christ's sake, fifty."

More shouting in Japanese then, surprisingly, "O.K. O.K."

Stock shook his head. "Let's hope that means he got it." To the watchkeeper. "Watch him." He checked the boat's range. Eighteen miles. Time, 11.10. Where the hell's that wave? Nothing showing at sixty miles. It must show on the radar. That pilot must've been out in his distances. Good. If that Jap turns now we might just make it. Go on, turn, you bastard. Turn and run and we'll pick you out of the water. That'll make me look sick but no matter. He shouted again into the R/T. "Have you changed course? o—5—o. Fifty degrees. Nor'east a half east. Fifty." He stared at the radar to pick up the boat's course. Come on, come on. That's it. Clever little Jap. You got the message. You've maybe just saved your Nipponese life.

He pushed himself back into his chair and drew breath. And how about you, Commodore Lang? You're doing fine down there, parading up and down, judging the roll to a nicety, never lurching or stumbling. Very pretty. You've given your orders and that's that. I was wrong about you. You're not Captain Bligh at all. You're Captain Ahab. And your big white whale's that wave, or that Jap, or both. Let's hope you don't go Ahab's way.

The watchkeeper tapped Stock's arm and pointed at the radar screen. It was there, just coming on at the extreme range of sixty miles. They both stared at it. It was just a thick line on the screen. Like a landfall, a cliff or sharply rising ground. But it was moving. It was moving as they watched. Fast. Very fast. 11.15. The Jap was fifteen miles away.

"Time it," snapped Stock. "And quick." He raised his voice for Lang. "Wave's on the radar at sixty miles. Looks like the side of a house."

The commodore just nodded and went on pacing.

Mike spoke to the boat. "Step on it, will you. Hurry up. D'you savvy that? Full speed."

The Japs jabbered in answer. "O.K. O.K."

"A hundred knots, sir," reported the watchkeeper. "I don't believe it but it's true."

Stock spun the calculator on the desk. Sighted 11.15. Sixty miles. A hundred knots. We're doing eighteen knots. Call it twenty; that gives us a margin. A hundred and twenty knots. Impact in thirty minutes, that's 11.45. Target fifteen miles, closing at say thirty knots. Half an hour. 11.45 again. We won't make it. We'll all meet, wave, fishermen and *Emperor*. All together. Wait. That wave speed's still not definite. Maybe, just maybe we can make it.

11.20. Target, twelve and a half miles. Drawing to starboard again. Wave at fifty-one miles.

"Give him a rocket," ordered Stock. "Two." He felt the thump of the rockets leaving as he bawled into the R/T. "See the rockets. Steer on the rockets." He spoke without turning.

"Reload." Again to the boat. "Steer on the rockets. You're off course. The rockets." Two more rockets soared up and trailed away aft into the silvery sky.

At the console they watched and waited, checking times and distances. Lang kept pacing up and down.

Sonia sat through it all, uncomfortable in her life jacket, cushions ready to stuff between herself and the table. She was tensed, her heart beating wildly, not understanding all of what was going on but knowing it was urgent, critical. Out there was that wave and between it and the *Emperor* were some fishermen whose only chance was to reach the huge tanker and abandon ship and be picked up before that wave caught them. She heard Mike shouting orders, she sensed him there beside her, but it was the commodore she watched. He's so calm. It's as if this is just a walk in the park for him. Maybe more normal because it's at sea and on a ship. She felt a touch on her shoulder. She turned. It was Gene. He gave a small smile and nodded to her. He reached out and put a hand over one of hers. Dear Gene. You're calm too. Or you look it anyway. That's your way. Even if you were afraid you'd never show it. Stiff upper lip. You're more British than the British, my darling. She smiled back at him.

11.25. Target ten miles. On course. Wave forty-three miles.

Stock shook his head. He's not going to make it. There must be a time lag. They've got to get off and we've got to pick them up. It needs a miracle now. He spoke down to the commodore. "It's no use, sir. We can't reach him in time."

Lang looked up briefly. "Full ahead, Captain. There's time."

Stock just stared. What the hell. Now we're bow on to the wave. That's how we've got to meet it. Time yet to drop the speed. Maybe there will be a miracle. Maybe old Christ down there will jump overboard and walk on the water and flatten out the wave. Some hope, he thought, as he watched the screen wide target advancing on the radar. He checked again in his

mind on what would be needed. It would be one hell of a
crash but there was a good chance. If. There was an awful lot
of ifs. He recalled Lang's phrase. No ifs or buts. If only that
was ever true.

11.30. Target seven miles. Wave thirty-four miles.

"In sight, sir."

"What?" Stock grabbed the binoculars.

"The boat, sir. Dead ahead."

Mike found it at once. Even end on, it was recognisable. It
was one of the deep sea Jap fishermen. There were boats like it
based on Shinoto. Away for weeks at a time. Shinoto. That's
funny. I haven't thought about Shinoto for an age. How long?
God, only just over a day. A whole day and I never once
thought about Kim. Wonder how she is. Wonder if that wave
going the other way will pound that breakwater. They'll
be safe. They'll know all about it. That boat's certainly doing
its best to stay alive. He moved the glasses to keep it in view as
the *Emperor* dipped in the swell and the fishing boat raced
ahead, plunging and bucking.

"Boat's in sight, sir," he called to Lang.

The commodore stopped and stared ahead through the
window. He picked it out quickly and nodded his head. So
much for the great Captain Stock. All right at Castle Brainwash but not so great on a ship at sea. Competent, yes; when
he's given the right orders. Can carry them out. Can't make the
decisions. This will put him in his place. There's the ship and
the men he wanted to leave to die. When this is all over he'll
know never to cross swords with me again. "Stand by to pick
them up," he ordered without looking round. "Switch in the
R/T down here, Captain. I'm going to bring him in on the
starboard side. They'll have to jump for it."

"You've got the R/T," said Mike. And good luck, you crazy
old bastard. If you bring this off, you'll be a hero for all time.
If you live. He spoke to the operations room. "Watch on deck,

starboard side. Catch them as they jump. Then get to hell off that deck." He watched the radar. Just as well old Lang can't see the echo that wave's throwing back.

11.39. Target three miles. Wave nineteen miles.

"Look, sir." The watchkeeper was staring ahead through the window.

Stock looked. It was in sight. He put the glasses up. It did not look very terrifying. It was as if the horizon was raised up. But as he watched he saw the crest, curling white, spilling down the front slope, blending, being overtaken by a new crest. It seemed to get bigger as he watched. He put the glasses down. God. "Wave's in sight, sir."

"Keep her going," bawled Lang. "I see no wave." He was standing quite still, watching the fishing boat, gripping the window ledge.

Stock spoke quietly into his microphone. "Chief, stand by to drop the speed."

11.40. Target two miles. Wave fifteen miles.

The R/T speaker suddenly burst into life. The voices were strident, desperate, panic stricken. It was a terrifying sound.

"They've seen it," shouted the watchkeeper.

Mike nodded. And no wonder they're scared. Look at it. The wave had shape now, vast, unbelievable shape and size. The front sloped steeply, curving forward at its peak in a drooping line of white and green. In the time it took to look and wonder, it was a mile nearer. Everyone on the bridge saw it now. Everyone but Lang. His eyes never left the fishing boat. The others saw and stared. It was the same frightened hypnotic stare as a pointed gun might bring on. But that wave was far more menacing than any gun.

"Now hear this, hear this. Six or seven minutes till that wave hits us. All but the watch on deck, take your places. All but the watch on deck, take your places. Face aft, back to bulkhead. Don't move, don't panic."

196

The Japanese were yelling frantically on the bridge speaker. The commodore lifted his microphone. "Quiet there. Quiet." The tone of command was enough to stop the babble. "Keep quiet and listen carefully. When I tell you, you will turn hard to starboard. Keep your engines at full speed. I repeat. Keep engines at full speed. Turn hard to starboard when I tell you. Not now."

"O.K. O.K."

Lang spoke up to Stock. "A point to port, Captain. Tell the chief to stand by the engines."

"Port a point it is, sir. The chief's ready."

11.42. The Jap was one mile off, fine on the bow. The wave was less than twelve miles away. Six minutes. Not long.

Lang barked into the R/T. "Hard a starboard now. Now. D'you hear? Now."

"O.K."

It seemed an age before the boat started to show her port side. Then quickly she was broadside, then showing her quarter. At full speed, even with her tight turn, she had set down almost a quarter of a mile nearer the tanker. The *Emperor* had run up half a mile on her. There were only two cable lengths between the ships. 11.44. The wave was eight miles off. Four minutes.

"Stop engines," ordered Lang into the R/T. "Stop engines now. Now."

"O.K. O.K."

"Jump when you're alongside. Jump. D'you understand? Jump when I tell you."

"O.K."

"Stop engines, Captain." This to Stock. "You con her now. I'm going out to the wing." He did not even look round. His eyes were fixed on the boat. He reached for a hand hailer and walked out to the starboard side.

11.45. The Jap was almost alongside. The wave was at six miles. Three, four minutes.

Stock pulled the *Emperor* round to starboard. As her bow swung in towards the Jap, her way carried her up on him. The boat was alongside, midships, but dropping astern. "We're over-running her. Put her engines ahead."

In the wing of the bridge, Lang did not need Stock's advice on the public address. He was already bawling down to the Jap skipper. "Full ahead. Full ahead." He saw the puff of the exhaust at the funnel top as the boat's engines were started up. It dropped back, steadied, then surged ahead. The gap closed as Mike edged the tanker close in. The fishermen were crowded round the little wheelhouse, staring wide-eyed at the huge ship towering over them.

"Jump," roared Lang. "Jump."

The group on the boat deck hung back, crowding together, all afraid to be the first to leap for the dangling grab nets.

"Jump. Jump."

The boat rolled to port and crashed into the *Emperor*'s side. One man jumped as the boat heeled back from the impact. The gap between the two ships widened. The man disappeared from view from up on the bridge. Everyone on the bridge was watching through the great circle of glass. There was a gasp. Then they saw the deck watch leaning over the side, stretching out. The man must have got a hold of the grab net low down. He was being helped up. Stock had the tanker's engines at Slow Ahead, trying to hold the boat alongside. The Jap skipper was using his head. He was keeping his engines going, matching the *Emperor*'s speed. The first Jap was up on deck. Four more jumped on to the net. Lang watched it all, hand hailer at the ready. He gave few orders.

The one man on the *Emperor*'s bridge who was not staring back and down at the boat all the time was the senior watchkeeper. Stock had given him the task of measuring the wave's distance on the radar. "Four miles."

Two more across on to the grab nets and up on deck. Seven saved. There was one left on the boat's deck and the skipper, hanging out of the wheelhouse window screaming at him to jump. He cringed back. Lang was bellowing to the men on the tanker's deck. A rope was thrown. The skipper ran out of the wheelhouse and caught it. He flung it round the man and tied it off. The *Emperor*'s men heaved on it and dragged the terrified fisherman off the boat and up on to deck. Eight saved. Just the skipper now.

"Two miles, sir."

Stock barked into the public address. "Tell him to stop his engines before he jumps." He saw Lang nod and raise the hailer. Let's hope that Jap gets the message. It's going to be bad enough without having a crewless boat running into that wave alongside us.

The skipper was outside the wheelhouse, judging the roll, waiting for the moment to jump. He hesitated and looked up as the commodore shouted at him.

Lang roared again. "Stop your engines."

The Jap scrambled back into the wheelhouse. As he came back on deck, the puffing exhaust died. He looked up at the tanker, then back at his own boat. It was seconds before he could make up his mind to jump. It was his boat, his livelihood. Maybe it was a life's work, all his savings. The boat started to drift aft.

"One and a half miles, sir," reported the watchkeeper.

"Jump, man," shouted Lang. "Jump."

The skipper looked up and nodded. He swayed with his boat as it rolled. Someone threw a rope. He grabbed it and jumped.

Stock did not wait. He slammed the *Emperor*'s engines to Full Ahead to surge away from the fishing boat. He looked up to get his bearings on the wave.

"One mile, sir."

Stock gaped. The wave had real size now. It was monstrously big. Its soaring front slope seemed to tower up to the sky, where the foaming crest curled, slithered off, reformed, slithered off again as if drooling in expectation of a feast. He glanced back and down on to deck. The last Jap was on board. "Get off that deck. At the double." The boat was already astern, clear.

There was very little time. Stock's eyes flickered between the instruments and the terrifying view ahead. He had the *Emperor* lined up. He cut the engines back to Dead Slow.

"Half a mile, sir."

Stock waved his hand to shut up the watchkeeper. From now on it would all be by eye and instinct. As he glanced down at the controls, he caught sight of the commodore down on the bridgefront. He was standing there, drawn up straight, staring up at Stock. It was all there in his eyes and his mouth and his jaw. It was all said better than in any speech. "Nine men, Captain Stock. Nine men saved whom you'd have left to die."

Mike shouted as his fingers moved on the controls. "Yes, yes. You're a bloody marvel. Now let's see a second miracle. Look out there. Behind you. Ahead."

Lang turned and stared. The sight of the wave transfixed him. He had forgotten all about it. His hands clutched for and gripped the window ledge as he looked straight into the face of the wave. It was the whole view ahead. It was all rearing, frothing, seething water. It was a moving precipice.

"Hear this, hear this. Soon now, soon now."

Sonia too had forgotten about the wave. She had watched the rescue, her heart beating wildly, her stomach screwed up into a tight little knot. She had lived through it with every leaping Jap, clenched her fists as each figure disappeared from view, then felt sick with relief as each man appeared over the edge of the tanker's deck, crawling and being hauled to safety up the grab nets. Then her eyes had fixed on the commodore as he came in from the bridge wing. She could not help staring. Here was a man who had dared everything and performed a miracle. It was Mike's shouting at Lang then his final command on the public address that brought her eyes ahead. The sight of the wave took her breath away. She had thought it was all over. Now she seemed to be staring at certain death. She shut her eyes and flung her head face down on the console table. Her mouth opened to scream but all that came out was a long terrified gasp.

Mike was right beside her. He heard her in the sudden stillness of the bridge. He glanced to his left and saw her stretched out, head down. Good girl. "Hear this, hear this. Brace yourselves." He looked ahead. The wave was very close, its speed no longer obvious. It seemed to be hanging there ahead, waiting to devour the ship. "Get down, Lang. Get down."

The commodore did not move. He was standing rigid at the window.

"Quartermaster. Get the commodore. Get him on deck. Get him."

The quartermaster scrambled up and lunged across the bridgefront. He hit Lang with all his weight and wrapped his arms round him and fell to the deck.

The wave was only seconds away.

CHAPTER SEVENTEEN

There was no time before the wave for Mike Stock to think about the commodore. He saw his order obeyed, the quartermaster hurling himself across the bridgefront, grabbing Lang and pulling him down away from the window. That was all he needed to know.

Stock's hands were on the engine and rudder controls. Both propellers were turning at Dead Slow. He prayed that her speed would be low enough to stop her driving hard into the face of the wave. He wanted the *Emperor* to ride up on the front slope, reduce the height of that wall of water, then dig in her bows, break into the wave below the crest, then fight her way through to the other side. That would need power, all the power of both engines, for the wave was travelling at near to a hundred knots and there were thousands of tons of it. But all the power of the engines would be useless if the propellers were not sunk in water they could grip and churn and drive away behind them. That too was part of the plan. If the ship met the wave right there would be water round the propellers at the critical moment. If she did not meet it right, if anything went wrong, and there were countless incalculable factors, then the stern would be high out of the water, the screws would race as they thrashed the air, and the ship would be at the mercy of the wave. Even if her entry was right and the propellers could drive her ahead at the correct moment with the right amount of power, there remained the problem of her length. She might get through the wave but in doing so she might break her back.

Mike had made his decision on that. He was committed now.

There was nothing he could do if he had been wrong. The only thing left in his control as the wave raced towards the ship was to get the line of entry right. The bow had to meet the sloping wall of water at exactly ninety degrees. Even a minute falling off of the bow would present a face to the wave. Given that face the wave would hit it, throw the ship off course, drive her broadside on, and overwhelm her.

Stock watched the bow. He would see or sense any movement before the click of the gyro recorded it. In watching the bow he had to look at the wave. Its front slope ran steeply up to the crest. The water was dark, streaked with foam, seeming to have a hungry energy of its own. It was very close now, the curling crest overhanging the ship like a soaring cliff. The angle of entry looked right. A split second to check. He looked left and right. Sonia had her head down on the table, ready for the impact. Gene and the two watchkeepers were crouched in their seats, their eyes staring ahead, as if hypnotised by the wave.

"Down," roared Stock. "Down."

The three men reacted at once. Their heads went down on to the console, their chests straining into the padding between them and the table edge just as the front of the wave ran under the *Emperor*'s bow.

Mike crouched in his seat. He dare not take his eyes off the wave. Every communications channel in the ship was linked into his head set. The microphone an inch in front of his mouth would pass on his orders. There would be none. Orders were no good now. He had the ship under his hands. Anything that had to be done, he would have to do, and he would have to do it fast. Very fast. His mouth was dry, his heart beating wildly. His chest was sore as he pushed against the padding that might save his ribs in the impact. He watched the bow. It plunged on. The slope of the wave was all round it. "Get up, you bitch. Get your bow up. Rise. Go on, rise." He saw the water showing above the bulwarks on both sides of the bow. Christ. She's not lifting. She's going right in. "Get up," he roared. The bow rose as if in answer to his command. Almost imperceptibly at first. But it had lifted. And it went on rising as the wave slope ran in under the ship and prised her up. The *Emperor* had an upward tilt now. She was facing up the front slope of the wave. The crest was there above her, huge, curling over, constantly changing shape and colour, breathtaking, menacing.

Now. Stock slammed both the engine levers to Full Ahead. The power would not be in time to drive the ship into the wave. Her momentum had to do that. The power was for when she was in the wave. The power had to keep her straight and drive her through to the other side. He watched the bow. It was still rising. For a moment Mike had a vision of that bow rising till the *Emperor* was standing on her stern. Now, you bitch. Stop now and dive into that wave. The bow faltered, stopped, dipped. The ship rammed herself into the wave and the massive crest dropped on her decks.

Even before the full weight of the water hit her, Stock could feel the ship straining. She trembled throughout her quarter-mile of length. Every part of the huge structure picked up the sensation from the bow and passed it on right aft through to the stern. That sparked no fear in Stock. It made the *Emperor* seem alive, ready to react, ready to fight for her life. The fo'c'slehead disappeared as the wall of water collapsed on it. The fo'c'slehead, the samson posts, the foredeck. Then there was no vision. The whole midships island was immersed. It all seemed to happen separately but it took only a split second. All sensation was scrambled up together into one terrifying experience. There was the impact; as if the ship had rammed an island at full speed. The whole ship shuddered and shook, groaned and shrieked. All the padding and the careful positioning of those on board did not save them from having the breath knocked out of them. But it did save them from much worse. In the empty cabins and crew spaces, everything loose flew forward as if fired from a gun. Drawers, chairs, doors, clothes, bedding; everything moved and crashed and broke and ripped. There was the noise; the noise of wreckage, the noise of steel strained almost to breaking point, the noise of men shocked and cursing their fate. Over everything there was the noise of water. It roared, it hissed, it gurgled, it splashed. It was everywhere. The *Emperor* was inside the wave, surrounded by water, wholly submerged. There was no sight from the bridge. Even up there the water was all around, dark, noisy, angry at being sealed out, straining to burst its way into the ship. It squirted under and round doors, tore at valves and pipes, ladders and catwalks, smashed lifeboats, ripped dodgers and awnings, swirled and surged and strained again at the enclosed space.

Stock was ready for the impact but he had not realised how severe it would be. His padding saved him but he felt the breath whistling out through his mouth. His feet and his hands and his ears told him of the torture the ship was going through. He could see nothing through the great circle of window. Nothing but a dark swirling mass that was the sea. With no view, everything now had to be by feel. The ship was inside the wave. It had to break its grip and escape through to the other side or be carried with it, inside it, and inevitably die. The instruments were all working. The engines were both at full revs. Come on, come on. Poke your bow out the other side. Let me see the air and the sky. Let me see what's out there behind this wave. He felt it. He would never have heard the gyro in that bedlam, but he felt it. He felt the bow dropping off. He twisted the rudder control. He wanted to whirl it all the way over. He held back. If he corrected too much, the ship might swing hard the other way and be swept on to lie broadside in the wave. It still dropped away. He felt it but he held himself in check. Voices were roaring in his ears about water leaking in all over the ship. Nothing. That was nothing. A bit of water could be dried up. But only if the ship lived. Come on, you bitch. Come back. She came. Slowly, fighting all the way. But she came. He took the rudder back to midships.

Then he felt it again. Not the bow being pushed off course. The bow dropping. Down. He knew what it was. He felt good. Then sick. It was dropping fast. Maybe too fast. The bow must be out through the back of the wave. But what was there? Nothing maybe. A huge following trough. A great yawning chasm for the ship to plunge into, bow first. Let me see. Let me see what it is. The bow dropped down. Then suddenly he could see again. Through the window, out of focus with the water streaming off the glass, but he could see. It was as if he was on top of a crevasse, looking down. Not on top but already falling.

He shouted and the microphone sent the warning through the ship. "Ready again. Here's another."

As the bow dropped into the dark pit, Mike picked up little details. The water ahead, black and green, moving but almost glass smooth on its surface. The water from the wave rushing forward on the fo'c'slehead, trapped by the bulwarks, trying to escape, swirling, frothing. Spume flying up and spattering the window. The bow dropped but seemed to reach out as the sea behind the wave moved on. The bow was almost down into the trough. It was starting to pull up, to get support, to slow its dive. Then the forefoot pounded down on to the front of the next wave. The whole weight of the *Emperor* at full power was behind it. It was as if the water was solid. The ship juddered through her whole length. Every hand gripping a table top or a chair arm, every foot straining against a deck or a bulkhead felt the shock. It jarred and rippled through everything and everyone. The bow sank into the wave like a cleaver slicing open a carcass. The sea divided, reared up on either side and crashed over and on to the deck. There was noise and shock everywhere. But the bow stopped dropping. It faltered then lifted. It kept on rising, and the water rushed and gushed and tried to escape back to the sea. The wave sped on across the ocean, astern.

Mike waited a few seconds. It took him that time to realise the ship had come through. It took him that time to feel that she was alive, that she had power on her screws and water on her rudder, that she had been bent up and down like a rapier under test and had not cracked. He was sure. He was sure she was still in one piece and under control. But he was going to check. He was going to check everything.

"Now hear this, hear this. That's probably the worst of it over. But don't be too sure. There may be secondaries still to come. Hold your positions. Everyone stay where you are. Report in now. Operations room first. That midship joint. Then you, George, on the engine room. Then any casualties. Go ahead."

He sat back in his chair and listened. He pulled the engines back to half speed then signed to the senior watchkeeper to take over the bridge controls and keep the ship on her present heading.

As he listened, Stock looked around. The other watchkeeper was sitting up and checking the console controls. Gene North was up in his chair, pale, dazed looking. Sonia was swung round, her head pushed against her husband, her arms tight round him, her back heaving as she sobbed her heart out. Lucky girl, thought Mike. Wish I could let off steam like that.

Down on the bridgefront, the commodore was on his feet, looking round, nodding his head. He looked up at the console deck and nodded vigorously. Mike could not hear him through the headset but he could read the words on his lips. "Good man. Good man." The reports were good. The joint had held. The engine room was in fine shape. Casualties—a few cuts and bruises, maybe one or two broken limbs. Nothing really.

The watchkeeper was tapping Stock's arm and pointing ahead. A new mound of water was rolling towards the *Emperor*. "Hear this, hear this. There's a secondary coming. Doesn't look too bad. Hold your places. Brace yourselves."

The wave moved in under the bow. The ship lifted easily and stretched out across the sea. It was not a wave. It was a huge swell, high but not too high, long and flat-topped. The water welled up round the ship, not breaking over the decks, but spouting through the scuppers and slopping lazily on board through the rails. After the wave, it was an anti-climax.

Then Mike froze. It was unbelievable. But it was happening. The flat top of the swell was showing a deep furrow. An ever-deepening furrow. The swell was not a swell. It was two huge waves run into each other, now separating again. The furrow became a deep trough, then almost at once a chasm. The *Emperor*'s bow sat on one crest, her stern on the other. In between, under that midship joint already weighed down with the concentration of ballast, the sea was scooped away as the two waves were reformed with a yawning ravine between their crests. There was no noise to it other than the sound of the heaving sea. None of the noise expected as a prelude to disaster.

Then the *Emperor* broke her back.

Stock felt it go. Everyone midships felt it; it was a feeling, an impression through eyes, ears, fingers, feet. No one but Stock recognised it for what it meant but everyone knew it was ominous. Mike knew the joint had given way. He had seen that trough forming, he had lived for four days with growing doubts about the joint's ability to withstand extreme stress. But he had no time now to think about it. A split-second later the disaster was apparent by its effects.

"Console's dead, sir," reported the watchkeeper. "No power."

Stock spoke into his microphone. "Take her over, Chief. We've lost control midships." No answer. "Chief, George, are you there?" The line was dead. All power, every communication channel to the stern had been torn out. Mike grabbed for the emergency walkie-talkie. "George, George, come in. Take her over from aft. Take her over from aft."

"I've got her, Mike. What the hell's happened?"

"The joint's gone. Drop her to Dead Slow. Just enough to give her headway. Take the steering till we get down aft."

"Got it."

"Don't move," roared Stock to everyone on the bridge. "Stay where you are." The ship was plunging across the second crest and down into the trough behind. With the joint wrecked, the two parts of the ship moved with the sea like the leaves of a loose hinge. Water burst over the bow and swept the length of the decks. The trembling was not now the protest of a ship straining in a seaway. It was evidence that deep inside her hull the *Emperor* was tearing herself apart. No one spoke. The only sound was the gushing water and the muffled shriek and hammer of the joint's hydraulic dampers run amuck.

The ship floundered awkwardly but pulled herself up out of the trough. Ahead the ocean looked flat. No huge waves, just that ever-present Pacific swell. But lethal enough to murder the crippled ship.

Suddenly, everyone was shouting.

"What happened?"

"She's a goner."

"She's coming apart."

The whistles on the voice pipes were screaming. From the operations room. "Everything's dead here. What do we do?" From the wireless room. "D'you want a Mayday?"

Stock was on his feet, shouting above the din. "Quiet. Quiet everyone." The noise died and faces were turned towards him. "That's better." To the watchkeepers. "Get aft and take the steering from the chief. Keep her heading into the swell." To the operations room. "Get down on deck and set the valves to empty the midship tanks. Then get aft." To the Sparks. "Forget it, your power's dead. You'll reach no one round here with these batteries. Get aft and wait." To the others. "Everyone else aft. And step on it." To the quartermaster. "Check that everyone gets aft. Don't forget these Japs. They're down below somewhere." He grabbed the walkie-talkie and jumped down the ladder to the bridgefront. "Hallo, George. Start the pumps to empty the midship tanks. We're setting the valves for you up here. Then come midships. I'll need your help. There might be just a chance."

The bridge was emptying. There was no panic, just urgency. The commodore was there beside Stock, his face grey and wet with clusters of sweat. "I told you that joint was no damned good. I told you, didn't I?"

"Yes, yes, you told me. Now get down aft and try and save half your ship."

"I knew it was no good. I told you."

"All right, all right. You told me. Let's leave the post-mortems till we're sure we're not all dead. Get aft while I see what I can do."

"There's nothing you or anyone else can do."

"I'm going to try. What's the matter, Lang? D'you want to be the only hero round here? Get aft." He pushed the commodore through the door to the top of the ladder. The bridge was empty. Mike went back and lifted a torch and hooked it on to his belt.

As he went down the outside ladders, Mike saw the catwalk to the stern with its line of hurrying figures. On the main deck, crewmen were whirling valve wheels. All around there was that eerie silvery light from the sun still struggling with the pumice cloud. The sea was dark, almost black, scarcely rippled by the puffing wind, but heaving lazily all the time. It looked an innocent sea but the noise and vibration, shrieking and trembling up from inside the ship, gave the lie to that.

George Moffat was waiting down on deck. "Sounds hopeless, Mike."

Stock just nodded and led the way into the centrecastle. The noise was worse there, concentrated. With the door open down to the access tunnel to the joint compartment on the port side, it became bedlam. There was no chance of talking there. They unlocked and swung back the door of the compartment. It was then that they got the whole noise of disintegration, unshielded. It was like being inside an anvil. Their faces screwed up against the din. Their torches flashed out and probed round the chamber. All the hydraulic rams had burst open the pistons in which they moved. With each movement of the ship, the rams were hurled in and out. With no resistance to slow and control them they were just like pile-drivers, wrecking everything in their path. The huge rods connecting the two halves of the ship were still in place but, with no control, they must soon be torn from their seats. The two men stepped back and slammed the door. They hurried round to the starboard side. It was the same story there. They went back up on to deck. It was half a minute before they could speak.

"What a bloody mess," said Stock, shaking his head and pressing his fingers into his ears.

"You can say that again. That lot won't last long."

"Anything we can do?"

The chief shook his head. "No, nothing. Maybe pray."

"I'm not really the type, George. What about flooding both the compartments? Wouldn't that damp down the movement a bit?"

"Water's not much good for that. Wait, though. You've maybe got an idea there. Not water but oil. There's plenty fuel oil."

Mike nodded. "Yes, fuel oil. And anything else there is.

Paint, grease, lube. Cement too. That should make a good stiff brew."

"It's a chance, Mike. Pretty slim but it might just work."

Stock was already talking into his radio. "All spare hands to the centrecastle. Jump to it." He handed the radio to Moffat.

"Chief here. Set two cargo pumps to flood the joint chambers with bunker fuel. We'll go in over the top."

Mike was already across the deck, spinning valves to set the lines. The crew came running along the catwalk and he shouted orders as he worked. "Get the cement. Every bag there is. Dump it into the joint chambers. Then paint, grease, the lot. You and you. Down here and strip the blanks off these lines. You three, into the centrecastle. The two longest hose lengths there are. Connect them here." In seconds the whole deck midships was a flurry of running, straining, heaving figures. No one had to be told. They were suddenly hoping to stay alive. Through it all, they were spurred on by the noise surging up from under their feet. Mercifully, there were no more big swells.

In ten minutes, fuel oil was gushing into both chambers. Two lines of sweat soaked men were carrying bags of cement, drums of paint, barrels of grease and lubricating oil down into the access passages and emptying them into the chambers. There was no reduction in the sounds of chaos as the *Emperor* moved slowly through the water. But the ship was still in one piece.

Stock came aft when he knew everything possible was being done. He brought Gene North with him. He had found him humping paint drums with the rest of the crew. "Come on back aft. You'll get a coronary doing that at your age."

"You wanted all spare hands, Captain. I'm spare."

"Look, there's a knack to what you're doing. You haven't

got it. Thanks all the same but they'll get on faster without you. Anyway, we'll maybe need your advice. Come on."

The commodore was waiting for them, pacing the unfamiliar sundeck on top of the poop house. "What d'you think, Stock?"

Mike wiped his face with his sleeve. "I prefer not to. But you've still got a ship. More or less."

Lang shook his head. "Damned joint. Damned new-fangled nonsense. I told you I didn't trust it. I should have insisted."

"Well, you didn't. You never know, we might make it. This seems to be our day for miracles."

The commodore turned to Moffat. "Chief, how soon can you give us back power midships? Or give Sparks some help to rig a transmitter back here?"

"Can't we wait a bit, Commodore? We need every man we've got on that joint just now. Sparks is up there too, chucking cement bags around like he was Tarzan."

"All right. But as soon as you can."

"Anyone for coffee?" It was Sonia. She had a tray of china mugs.

"That's a clever girl," said Mike. "Just what the doctor ordered."

They all helped themselves.

"How does it look up there now?" asked Sonia.

"Not bad, not good," Mike told her.

She nodded. Everyone's alive and the ship still seems to be in one piece. That's something. The thought did not make her feel much better. There was no guarantee of how long it would stay that way. She moved on with her tray. Keep busy. Keep doing things. Don't think about it. She had been telling herself that ever since that run along the catwalk to the poop with the ship seeming to be coming apart under her feet. She had started at once to bathe the cuts and bruises and splint the broken limbs from the wave. She had talked to the frightened Japanese who did not understand what she said but seemed pleased she was talking to them. Then when all the crew ran off midships she had started making coffee. Anything to keep from thinking about what might happen and from remembering the sight of that wave and the terror of staring at what seemed certain death and feeling and hearing it clawing at her and dinning in her ears. All she wanted now was to get off the ship and never even look at the sea again. But she dare not think that blissful thought. It was still a long way off. Maybe out of reach.

The commodore was sipping his coffee. "Just as soon as you can, Chief. I must get a distress call out. Even if that joint holds for a bit, we're going to need help."

"There won't be much help around here," said Stock. "It's not the busiest of shipping lanes, you know. Anyway, I doubt if anything else survived that wave."

"Then we must get a plane at least. Look around, man. There's hardly a serviceable piece of lifesaving equipment left on board." It was true. There had been no time to check up after the wave. Now they could see all the destruction it had done. All the boats were stoved in or twisted up in their mangled davits. A lot of the life rafts had been swept away off their skids. "So as soon as you can, Chief. Then we'll get a plane to drop some rafts and stand by us till a tug or another ship can reach us."

"No, Commodore." It was Gene North.

"Sorry, what was that?" asked Lang.

"I said 'No,' Commodore. No distress call. Nothing to give any hint that we may be in trouble."

"You're crazy." Lang could not hold it back.

Gene shook his head. "No, Commodore, I'm not crazy. This ship is still in one piece. In an emergency there are probably enough life rafts to go round. If the front half does break off, am I not right in believing that the stern would still float?"

"Maybe yes, but . . ."

"But nothing. This ship is just one part of a much bigger project. Any hint of trouble could knock millions of dollars off the company's shares and jeopardise years of work. I won't allow that."

Lang gaped at him for seconds before he found his voice. "You're not in a position to allow or disallow anything on board this ship. I'm in command. I give the orders."

"Of course you do, Commodore. But I'll tell you what orders to give. When the radio is back in action, you will send a cable announcing that we survived that wave. You will also say that you saved the whole crew of a Japanese fishing boat. You will then say that you have suffered only superficial damage and are returning to Japan for repairs." Gene turned to Stock. "Captain, I want to be sure that you also understand what I've just said."

Mike shrugged his shoulders. "I get the point. Nothing but a plane could get near us for days anyway. We might as well wait a few hours till we see what's going to happen with that joint. But you're taking a hell of a chance."

"They pay me for taking chances, Captain." Gene looked round from Lang, to Moffat, back to Stock. "How would you rate our chances, Mike?"

"As they say in Inoco, nothing's impossible. But I wouldn't quote you odds."

CHAPTER EIGHTEEN

The official version of that Inoco motto ran: The difficult we do immediately, the impossible takes just a little longer. For those on the *Emperor*, a little longer was nine nerve-racking days. Nine days, nine nights, two thousand miles of heaving water till suddenly, unbelievably, land smudged the horizon ahead, quickly grew, took shape, was recognised. Japan. Shinoto.

It had taken a lot of experiment to find the right speed for the ship. They had found that at nine knots she rode the swell best, putting the least possible strain on the hull midships. Everyone on board had become accustomed to the idea of the *Emperor* living from minute to minute, hour to hour, with only two chambers of filthy slurry saving her from ripping herself apart. The weather had been kind. Shifting the ballast water had helped too. They had had to judge it all by sound and feel. They never got rid of all the vibration but they cut it down. The sound too had stayed with them. It was a constant low-pitched growl deep inside the hull, the kind of sound that quickly becomes a part of life. But every so often it suddenly became a roar and a shriek as the ship misjudged a swell. Then breath was held, senses keyed, till the comforting growl returned.

Each new day, with the ship still intact and sailing, was a reason to be pleased and thankful. None of the men on board felt that way. They all knew, but never admitted, that the *Emperor* could fall part under them at any time. By not talking about it they tried to ignore it.

Sonia North was the exception. She quickly accepted the

216

fact that the ship was still whole and making for safety. For her, every minute was not the last before disaster. It was one minute nearer the land. She talked. Maybe too much. She was gay. Maybe too gay. But she could not be ignored. She was a diversion; she was invaluable.

The power had been restored to the bridge as soon as the work on the joint was finished. Sparks got the wireless gear going and the cables started to flow. There had been the plain language one telling of the wave and the rescue of the fishermen. There had been ones to London and New York, in Gene North's special codes, telling the whole story of the damage. There had been replies, congratulating them on the rescue, congratulating them on their good sense in keeping the details of the real damage secret. There was something good for everyone in these cables. Their effect was short lived.

There was plenty to worry about on board. For the first few days there had been the knowledge that they were travelling back along the course they had come, back nearer to where Phoenix Island had been, not knowing what new terror might be brewing up under the ocean. Every roar from the joint, every bigger than usual swell, had been a new threat. When that danger was past, it only left more time to brood on what had happened, why it had happened, who was responsible, and how the blame would be laid. It was never discussed. There was no post-mortem on board. The three men most concerned thought their thoughts privately.

On the face of it, Gene North had little to worry about. The pages of his journal told a different story. It had been his decision not to broadcast their plight. It had been the right decision. But because of that decision, no ship had come to stand by the *Emperor*. Each day North remembered that, if the ship did not make it back to Japan, every lost life would be his responsibility. And one of those lives could be his wife's. He worried too about another decision he had made a long time before. He worried about his decision to overrule Bruce and appoint Lang to command the ship. He recalled his motives; he had done it just to remind Bruce who was the real boss. Till seconds before the wave, he was sure he had been right, even if for the wrong reasons. Seeing these Japanese snatched from certain death, Gene had been certain he had chosen well. Now he knew that Lang would never have got the ship through that wave. Now he knew that but for Stock and the chief engineer, the *Emperor* might only be an echo of the Lutine bell at Lloyd's. One thing pleased him. Jim would not be thinking about another job now. Not till his project was proved. And if it was not proved, no one in the oil business would want to know his name. But that went for Gene too. He wondered what it all might mean when it was assessed in the cold clear atmosphere of the boardroom in New York. He had staked everything on Project Emperor. If it failed or even faltered, his life's work would come to an abrupt end. There would be plenty of volunteers to speed him on his way.

The commodore had found it difficult to accept that his ship had survived the wave and the trough and was still whole and moving ever nearer safety. But he worked hard at justifying to himself his every action. He had been right about turning back into the wave. There were nine Japs to testify to that. He had been right in leaving Stock to take the ship through the wave. It was a job for the man up at the control console. But was that wave faster and bigger, were these secondary waves higher and more dangerous because he had turned the ship back? If he had kept her going the ship would have been thirty miles or more to the east when the wave caught it. How much would it have dropped in height and speed in that time? It was a theoretical exercise but it was what would be done ashore when the time for explanations came. He had been right too about asking for ships to stand by after the *Emperor* broke her back. He had allowed himself to be talked out of that. That hurt. He was in command. He should have made the decision. In the end, it was his responsibility. It was useless to plead that he had been ordered not to summon help by North. No one knew the rules better than John Lang. Worst of all, there were his doubts about the joint before the ship ever sailed. That would come out. How could he explain that he did nothing about it other than mention it to his staff captain? Yes, and there was Stock who was going to come out of it all as the glory boy, the man who took the ship through the wave, the man who found a way to save the ship when it seemed doomed. Yes, Stock, the man who sided with Gene North about these cables and made Lang's humiliation complete.

Mike Stock was not at all sure that he would come through the inquiry unscathed. He was certain he would not. When the test readings were examined, he would be asked why he had not recognised the potential hazards. He could plead that the differences were not statistically significant. He would be reminded that, in the event, they proved to be significant. Black mark. He would be asked about his refusal to turn back to the rescue of the Japs. He could argue that they were only saved with seconds to spare so his judgment had only been minutely in error. But they had been saved. Black mark again. He could argue that because the ship turned back, it met the wave earlier and was thus nearly lost. Small black mark for trying to shift the blame on to the commodore. Then there was his decision on how to distribute the ballast. He might get away with that. He had been right for the wave, wrong for the trough. There was, of course, the way he had brought the ship through the wave. Gold star. And saved her from breaking up. Another gold star. Fairly evenly balanced. Two and a half black marks against two shining gold stars. But there was something else. He had been chosen as the key man on the *Emperor*. He had a special brief from Bruce. Where the blame lay did not matter. Project Emperor had been put in jeopardy.

Jim Bruce did not like being let down by his key men. The sentence was a foregone conclusion. Mike had made up his mind for the worst. You can't win them all, he told himself. But there would be compensations. They were going back to Japan. Japan meant Kim. There were a lot of jobs. There were not many Kims.

The last cable came when the ship was still four days away from Japan. It was from Bruce. He was meeting the ship on arrival. They had all expected that. But seeing it written down gave a new edge to their worries. That cable did its job. Bruce wanted them all to sweat.

On that last morning, the sight of land and the growing detail of the headlands and the bay, the hill and the town scattered round its base, swept away all thoughts of anything but their individual safety. They had made it. It was all over. The *Emperor* moved slowly across the bay, rounded to, and the anchor chain roared out through the hawsepipe, checked, clattered, checked again and the brake on the windlass was screwed up tight. No one spoke. They were all feasting their eyes on the land.

Lang, the Norths, and Stock stood together in the wing of the bridge. Almost at once they saw the Yashawa tender coming out between the breakwaters. They watched it through their binoculars. They saw Bruce. He was standing on the open bridge of the tender, tall, erect, his auburn hair gleaming in the sunshine, his face solemn as ever, his eyes fixed on the *Emperor*. He was easily recognised. The years seemed to make no impression on him. He had looked the same since his early twenties. He would look the same when he was into his forties. He was a Peter Pan. Or maybe a Dorian Gray.

Gene North nodded slowly. Jim was in there fighting already. It was his project and he was going to save it. He would roll as many heads as need be. I'm a fool, he thought. What am I worried about? I'm his boss. If he saves himself, he saves me. That's logical. But is it? There's an obvious flaw in that argument. North lowered his glasses. He felt uneasy.

The commodore paid little attention to the tender. He knew he would never sail in command again. His time was up anyway in less than two months. It would all be disguised by his retirement. He would have to face Bruce but he would admit to nothing. Lang's eyes were riveted on that towering hotel and the temple-like penthouse perched on its roof. He was remembering Mr. Yashawa. He knew he was going to hear again of his death. He knew he was going to live again all his doubt and guilt. He was going to wonder if he had driven the old man to take his own life. He was going to remember that medal ribbon, worn proudly, unearned, undeserved.

Stock could not believe his eyes. He gave Bruce only a brief look. It was the other figure on the tender that held his attention. You were right, Mike. Jim doesn't like his key men to let him down. He'll get on, that one. He's a proper bastard.

All that mattered to Sonia was the land close by. She could smell it. She was desperate to put a foot ashore on it, to make quite sure it was real. She saw the approaching boat, she saw and recognised Bruce. It meant nothing to her. She looked round at the three men beside her. She smiled and shook her head. She thought she could read their faces like an open book. Their concern for their careers and reputations seemed trivial compared with the simple fact of having survived, being safe at last. "Well, there's the great Mr. Bruce. He's not very frightening, is he."

Mike was the only one who took any notice. He gave her a small, wry smile.

"Who's the woman with him? I don't recognise her."

"No, you wouldn't," said Mike. "Her name's Janice. Janice Stock."

Sonia gaped at him. Janice Stock. Mike's wife. In Shinoto. She giggled. Then she laughed. She clutched at the bridge rail and hooted with mirth. And she went on laughing and laughing hysterically till her stomach ached and the tears started into her eyes and rolled down her cheeks.

Also by Marc Lappé

• • •

BROKEN CODE:
The Exploitation of DNA

WHEN ANTIBIOTICS FAIL

CHEMICAL DECEPTION:
The Toxic Threat to Health
and the Environment

LIFE'S GREATEST MIRACLE

EVOLUTIONARY MEDICINE:
Rethinking the Origins of Disease

THE
BODY'S EDGE

*Our Cultural
Obsession with Skin*

• • • • •

MARC LAPPÉ, PH.D.

*Henry Holt and Company
New York*

Henry Holt and Company, Inc.
Publishers since 1866
115 West 18th Street
New York, New York 10011

Henry Holt® is a registered trademark
of Henry Holt and Company, Inc.

Published in Canada by Fitzhenry & Whiteside Ltd.,
195 Allstate Parkway, Markham, Ontario L3R 4T8.

Library of Congress Cataloging-in-Publication Data
Lappé, Marc.
The body's edge: our cultural obsession with
skin / Marc Lappé.—1st ed.
p.   cm.   Includes index.
1. Skin—Physiology.   2. Skin—Anatomy.
3. Skin—Social aspects.   I. Title.
QP88.5.L37   1996   95-45978
612.7'9—dc20   CIP

ISBN 0-8050-4208-3

Henry Holt books are available for special promotions and
premiums. For details contact: Director, Special Markets.

First Edition—1996

Designed by Victoria Hartman
Printed in the United States of America
All first editions are printed on acid-free paper.∞
1   3   5   7   9   10   8   6   4   2

7/96 Ingram 12.60